MW00843609

SEARCHING
FOR GOLDILOCKS

SEARCHING FOR GOLDILOCKS

SEARCHING FOR JUST RIGHT
WITHIN AND ALL AROUND US

MATT KRESL, PharmD, BCPS

NEW DEGREE PRESS

COPYRIGHT © 2022 MATT KRESL
All rights reserved.

SEARCHING FOR GOLDILOCKS

Searching For Just Right within and All around Us

ISBN	979-8-88504-583-4	*Paperback*
	979-8-88504-928-3	*Kindle Ebook*
	979-8-88504-699-2	*Ebook*

To Lily, the girl I met once who showed me everything about searching for right.

CONTENTS

INTRODUCTION
WHY JUST RIGHT?

———

He who holds balance... has attained the highest post in the world.

—LAOZI

"I just want to get back to feeling normal again."

The belief in normal is both a reality and human creation. Those truths often collide when it comes to terms like "well-being" and "health," something I've spent my adult life trying to better understand as a caregiver and pharmacist. This is the framework for the trek we'll be on together.

Jim hit me as an example of that collision. He'd recently discharged from the hospital after a heart issue had put him in intensive care on a ventilator. My mind cycled through the odds, a habit it's developed when trying to understand how numbers help distinguish the random from the inevitable. My mental odds maker was focused on one fact in particular: about one-third of people who spend time on a hospital ventilator meet the definition of post-traumatic stress disorder (PTSD) at one month (Davidson et al. 2013). Would Jim be one of them?

We sat down to get reacquainted. I was surprised his concern was his back and leg pain, not his heart. But maybe I shouldn't have been surprised because he'd already seen other caregivers about his heart. As we talked, my mind began to ease a bit. He didn't appear deeply impacted by his recent hospital stay.

Even with that relief, I knew Jim was in a pickle. I told him his back pain had many causes, and his drugs didn't discriminate between them. I made it clear to him that there were no silver drug bullets. I wasn't sure if there were any silver drug linings either.

To his pain specialists, there were reasons to discriminate and be hopeful, to look closer at the pain origin sources. He told me they were now looking at placing a pain pump near his back. He understood this pump would ooze a small cocktail of medicines to provide additional pain relief. I knew it was the option chosen when many others had hit a dead end. He seemed to understand the same.

As we got to know each other, it was easy to root for Jim. In his formative years, some of them being on high doses of pain medicines, he was a man who went about setting and achieving goals. He'd done well in business and had a family. He had the voice of a guy who you imagined closing business deals. Despite his discomfort, he oozed a personality style intent on finding the positive.

In the end, we adjusted the dose of several pain medications to help around the margins. I encouraged him to go to cardiac rehabilitation, something he was reluctant to do at first. I shared how movement and a community may do his spirit some good, which he agreed would be helpful. I counseled him on what to ask his pain doctors—who he was meeting with later in the week—about the pain pump. We made plans to meet in the near future.

After the visit, I went back to my desk. What looped in my mind then, and for days after, was what "normal" meant. Jim likely made the comment, just as we all do, to explain a prior state of being when things were somehow better. I started to think maybe normal wasn't what Jim was looking for. Maybe normal isn't what any of us are looking for. I started to wonder if normal was a proxy for something else, something more at the heart of feeling whole.

"America's health care system is neither healthy, caring, nor a system," television news anchor Walter Cronkite once said (Rosenthal 2013). Walter Cronkite died in 2009, but I doubt he'd change one word of that quote if he were alive today.

Jim's story is not unique and makes it easy to dwell on the state of American health care. To some, there are simple realities to explain it: a body's decline over time, a lifetime of bumps and bruises, and corrupt pharmaceutical forces normalizing dangerous amounts of tranquilizers and sedatives. It's clear something is out of balance, and it's doubtful anything will ever change. But a ten-point policy plan to fix health care is not where Jim's story will take us.

Where we are going has everything to do with how we understand "normal." On one level, normal is pretty straightforward: normal is what's expected, typical, and standard. What's missing is that the modern world is moving at a pace where normal isn't anchored to anything expected, typical, or standard. Maybe past generations didn't have normal figured out, but the past one hundred years have ushered in communication, food, and travel changes that leave us expecting the unexpected (Diamandis 2017). It's clear something doesn't feel right. This feeling led me to search for something that helped me reframe normal in a whole new light. It's about seeing normal more as a "just right" instead of something to be expected.

Searching for Goldilocks requires explanation and a little personal history. Like many people, I was exposed to the story of *Goldilocks and the Three Bears* as a kid. It wasn't until I was in high school that I was introduced to something called the Goldilocks Principle. We'll get to the principle's details in the next chapter. I remember watching public television—before any nerd alert claims, remember this was the preinternet 1990s—where a scientist talked in front of a university crowd explaining how our planet was "just the right" distance from the sun. He went on to explain that our planet was in what was dubbed the Goldilocks Zone—not too hot, not too cold, but "just right" for sustaining life on Earth.

I was blown away on many levels. First was the name itself, the idea that a children's book theme could be co-opted to explain the reason for our existence—or, more importantly, *my* existence. Remember, I was an early teenager at the time. The totality of everything around me hinged on a sixty-seven-thousand-miles-per-hour rock cruising in a vast universe at the proper distance and speed from a big fiery ball (Herman 1998). What are the chances?[1]

As I got older, my mind then started exploring further. I learned this Goldilocks fact was anchored to other facts like

---

1   While there are no exact numbers available, the Drake Equation has tried to estimate it and 300 million has been speculated in the Milky Way alone (Gilster 2020). This number has been debated but certainly lends itself to the idea that we may not be alone.

the development of water, which then explained many other things I took for granted, such as the shower I took or the rain that grew the crops. It seemed like a big truth. Maybe *the* truth that all other truths hinged on. I started to wonder if principles like these were the normal I was searching for.

Since then, I've subconsciously internalized the notion of "just right," even if I didn't call it that. Exploring it for this book, I now appreciate it even further in the every day: music, nature, athletics, books, good company, or a timeless piece of art. There are a lot of words individuals use when describing these moments: wonder, awe, gratitude. It's also grounded me to another word I'm now using: right.

If normal doesn't feel like the word people are searching for, what about the expectation of being happy? If you look at the numbers, the average American's relationship to happiness seems as equally challenging as normal. According to the 2019 World Happiness Report, the United States has seen a ten-year decline in overall happiness in adolescents and adults. The 2019 report offered this sobering statement:

> *Several credible explanations have been posited to explain the decline in happiness among adult Americans, including declines in social capital and social support (Sachs 2017) and increases in obesity and substance abuse (Sachs 2018).*

The analytical side in me knows these reports are built on survey data, and survey data can be fickle and unreliable. But totality and trends matter, and one way of looking at just right seems more and more elusive even as the material wealth in the US increases.

In the following chapters, I will show happiness or normal are not the outcomes we need to examine. **The big idea of this book is that just right lives within and all around us.** The Goldilocks Principle helps us understand that "normal" is found in "just right" words like balance and equilibrium, that just right shows up in spectrums and shapes, and that just right involves a tension between forces that are always present. This will be about seeing the world a little differently in service to the search. With any hope, we will all be in a better relationship for it.

What will unfold in the following chapters will follow a familiar pattern. Many will start with the stories of people I've had the privilege of helping care for over the years. Their names, ages, and historical details have been altered to protect their identities. Some of them are still living, while others have passed away. Their quotes and concerns are an accurate representation of the challenges they expressed during our time together. Their stories serve as a launching point to the larger subjects of religion, storytelling, biology, death, health, numbers, self-help, communication, and economics that will reveal the just right theme.

Following the caregiver stories, I will examine their deeper significance using scientific evidence and pictures of the just rights within and all around us. Some of it will feel academic but will be in service to the broader themes that will emerge. For those who don't enjoy science and research, I promise to keep it interesting.

For the fellow science nerds, I want to acknowledge there are subjects I could explore deeper and with greater detail. I will not be completing an exhaustive review of any one subject. My inner critic acknowledges this could be seen as the work of a professional dilettante. My goal for the reader is simple: you could finish each chapter with a "yeah, but you forgot about…" or "yeah, but this is what I think about…" and I will consider that thinking a job well-done—of course, I'll probably never know such things. After all, this book is called *Searching for Goldilocks*, not Finding Goldilocks.

Finally, as the public television moment showed, I will delve into my own relationship to just right. I hope by showing my inner search that, I will inspire others to do the same. Where the science may inspire a "you forgot about…" my stories hopefully inspire an "I need to sort out my thought on…" As Jim's story showed, the people and stories we encounter are the seeds of the search. The just right amount of rainwater can help it grow.

It's time to get started. To understand just right further, we need to build a baseline understanding of science and storytelling. It will take surprising turns, but any searches worth taking are filled with the unexpected. Let's go meet Goldilocks and examine her principle a bit further.

PART 1

HOW WE GOT HERE: WHAT DO THE FORMAL AND APPLIED SCIENCES HAVE TO SAY ABOUT SEARCHING FOR JUST RIGHT?

CHAPTER 1

BACKGROUND—A GOLDILOCKS PRINCIPLE PRIMER

I have just three things to teach: simplicity, patience, compassion. These three are your greatest treasures.

—LAO TZU

What does Goldilocks have to do with the nature of life on Earth? Why are scientists in various disciplines taking an idea from a fairy tale to make larger points on scientific breakthroughs? This is something I briefly touched on in the introduction and promised to explore further. First, it's helpful to ground ourselves in the intersection between science and storytelling.

First, there's the storytelling part. When it comes to naming the Goldilocks Principle, it boils down to this truth: the best scientists know the power storytelling has in helping make sense of new knowledge. Humans are natural storytellers who relied on the medium long before words were ever written down. History has shown our species needs storytelling to find meaning, a form of "just right" within us to help explain the "just rights" all around us. In short, to understand a principle, we need to anchor ourselves to a story—stories as timeless as *Goldilocks and the Three Bears*.

I'll be coming back to the storytelling theme often, both the stories we tell ourselves and others throughout the book. But I'd be remiss if I didn't ground us all in the story that puts the idea of the principle into motion. It's a simple one with broad implications. Maybe you've heard it before? Its foundation reveals some fundamental truths to come. Let's go.

Goldilocks faced a dilemma. She set out into the forest alone for the day, a girl with a wild imagination looking for novelty and adventure. She stumbled onto a house she had never seen before, a wonderful structure tucked deep in the woods, visible only to those who knew its exact location. But when she knocked on the door of the strange house, she didn't get an answer.

Was nobody home? Surely somebody had to be here, she thought.

She could smell food coming from the window.

Why wasn't anybody coming to the door?

She thought about turning around. But being a curious and adventurous little girl, she decided to take a different path.

She saw the door was ajar and unlocked! This must be a sign. She entered the house and found freshly cooked porridge at the table, a nicely kept living room with chairs, and a bedroom with three beds for three creatures.

Amazing, she thought. *All the novelty she could ever want!*

With nobody around, she decided to indulge in the delights of her new surroundings. She tried all three bowls of porridge and found one that tasted best. She sat in all three chairs in the living room and found the one that was most comfortable. She laid in all three beds and found one to be the best to rest in. She took a nap on the bed, only to find the three bears who lived in the home staring at her when she woke.

In a panic, she leaped from the bed and ran home. Her adventurous spirit had gotten her into a scary predicament. She found her way home, huffing and puffing with fright. She told her worried parents what she had done and confessed her blunder. She lived to tell the tale, saying she'd never do such a thing again.

The end.

The story of *Goldilocks and the Three Bears* is one of the most endearing fairy tales in English literature. Details have been changed and adapted since its original draft by Robert Southey in 1837. In the original, the bears were not a mother, father, or child but instead three bachelor bears. The child was an old woman, then a fox. Some adaptations have taken on darker tones with the old woman or fox being killed (Tolovaj Publishing House 2021).

Future versions gave the story a lighter feel, inserting a young girl who was able to escape to her parents. Today's versions are as short as one minute and as long as ten minutes. The longer versions add character depth and dialogue to both Goldilocks and the three bears.

The story continues to evolve with modern versions of childhood curiosity, just right, and three choices being used elsewhere. In my research, I found versions of Goldilocks all over the world. I even found a version on YouTube that is set in Ghana called *The Ghanaian Goldilocks*, which features a boy whose curiosity gets the best of him.

The meaning of the story has also evolved over time. Some versions stress the "naughty, naughty girl" theme, a clear lesson that children should not go into strange places alone without supervision. Goldilocks broke the law by going into a house she did not own and found herself surrounded by large strangers (Hasa 2016). She should have been arrested! She could have died!

Other scholars highlight the bold and adventurous spirit of a girl following her curiosity, a lesson she was able to teach herself through action and escape (Tearle 2022). Let the lesson be the confession and the learning that comes from someone who's obviously frightened—even if we can't prove she learned her lesson at the end. If we put too many restraints on children, how will they ever learn for themselves?

Throughout different versions of the story, several themes have endured. The rule of three is in most versions and is a device often employed in storytelling, with Goldilocks having three choices in three different situations. Author Christopher Booker characterizes these three choices in his book *The Seven Basic Plots* as the dialectical three, where "the first is wrong in one way, the second in another or opposite way, and only the third, in the middle, is just right." Booker continues, "This idea that the way forward lies in finding an exact middle path between opposites is of extraordinary importance in storytelling."

There are three bears, three situations, and three choices for Goldilocks to choose from. Each of these is thought to help both the storyteller and the reader find a middle way. This middle way has later been adapted to represent the concept of "just right."

This is the genesis of how the word Goldilocks found its way from a fairy tale to a principle founded on the "middle path" or "just right." This is where my understanding of "just right" started. Most importantly, it's instructive on how storytelling helps us understand something fundamental that science can struggle to convey. Relating to the feeling of eating a perfectly warm chocolate chip cookie (or porridge in Goldilocks case) is easy, whereas relating to a 4.54-billion-year-old planet moving at inconceivable speed in a fourteen-billion-year-old constantly expanding universe is hard.

How we come to understand our own relationship to Goldilocks is tricky. We tell stories to ourselves, but—just like the fairy tale—the story gets rewritten and reinterpreted. Stories have the power to change, sometimes by family, friends, and people we love. Anchoring a story to a principle gives it a foundational truth, which makes the story of Goldilocks solid.

How I relate to the story of Goldilocks is complicated. Its reconstruction is a by-product of being far removed from childhood. Reexamining its meaning may be instructive to others who are on their own search. For me, it was instructive embracing both versions of Goldilocks and seeing the world needs both.

When I heard the story of Goldilocks as a kid, my instinct was not to focus on the porridge, the chair, or the bed. My childhood was shaped by the rules given by adults: be home by a certain time, turn in my homework, make my bed, go to church, and try to color inside the lines. However, I didn't grow up in a strict household. My parents were pretty easygoing, and they knew I was hard enough on myself. I think my temperament has always been to internalize the world this way.

As I got older, those rules became expectations I held onto: get a job, find a place to live, pay taxes, maybe start a family. Childhood was the preparation ground for learning the rules of adulthood that we need to follow.

It's easy to see how growing up helped me internalize one version of a fairy tale. Goldilocks did not follow the rules. She was a naughty girl.

Childhood me would have advised Goldilocks to control her adventurous spirit, so the adults thought she was a "good girl." The unwritten rules of childhood were to listen to adults so I didn't make mistakes. Nothing in childhood made me sadder than to let an adult—parent, teacher, coach, or relative—down. Letting myself down was another disappointment.

Revisiting the Goldilocks story as an adult, I realize how I missed something big. The story resonates only because "just right" is discovered in mischief. Yes, Goldilocks was "naughty," but how would she have learned otherwise? Or have anything to teach us? If there's no mischief, there's no story.

I realize now the tension between following rules and being adventurous is its own form of "just right." Forgetting to make the bed and coloring outside the lines has transformative power for the right person. Making their bed and coloring inside the lines has power for others. The challenge is in understanding the tension between the two and where someone lies at any given time.

Seeing the story through adult eyes has revealed other truths. One is that Goldilocks experiences the porridge, chairs, and beds through taste, touch, sight, and feel. Goldilocks has no friends or adults to tell her how to experience each; her body tells her all the just rights on its own. Sometimes adults fail to hang onto the childhood way of letting curiosity be their guide. I know I've often forgotten that lesson. Examining the story again has been a wonderful reminder.

Alright, it's time to switch gears from storytelling to truth telling, a theme that will emerge prominently in a later chapter. We are going to examine the Goldilocks Principle's far-reaching qualities to understand "just rights" all around us. It's a tour around science in the most unexpected of places.

Nod in agreement if this feels relatable. We need a new car, so we earnestly begin our internet search to find one. Online, we locate a make and model that's available, and we have to have it. Our search also reveals that there are no other cars like it on the lot or even in the city. We make a beeline to the car lot, take it for a drive, love it, and thank the stars we can afford it. We head inside to sign the paperwork, grab the keys, and drive off feeling very cool, very fortunate, and very unique. We are over the moon with our purchase! The cool feeling hangs on as does the thank the stars sentiment. Sadly, the unique feeling fades as soon as we get home. On our triumphant drive back, we notice all the people who have the same car as we do. We mutter to ourselves how stupid we must be: maybe there's a reason those car ads show up influencing my tastes? We try to shake off this tinge of disappointment. It's important for us to embrace the feelings of being cool and fortunate, even if unique isn't in the cards.

This story captures my relationship to the Goldilocks Principle. I feel cool and grateful for having come across it, but I realize—like the other cars—it seems to be everywhere. The just right Goldilocks Principle has been applied and adapted to a wide range of subjects from developmental psychology, biology, economics, and engineering (Fuchs 2021). Following are five examples I picked from the literature to show how the principle has been applied. It is by no means an exhaustive review. Hopefully, it doesn't come with the disappointment of driving home deflated.

Novelty versus Familiarity: Have you ever heard a child say, "I'm bored" or "This is too hard, I give up"? Note: Adults often think these things. We just rarely verbalize them. Children are truth tellers. Some evidence shows that this phenomenon may be hardwired into us.

In 2012, researchers out of the University of Rochester set up an ingenious study that was able to predict an infant's relationship to the concept of familiarity and novelty (Kidd et al. 2012). The way they did it was both simple and complex: they had parents place their infants on their laps, gave the parents headphones, showed the infants a sequence of predetermined images, then measured their eye movements using a special camera. Yes, these cameras do exist.

The image sequence and image designs mattered, as did the statistical modeling they used to control for confounders. But they were able to show a "Goldilocks" effect where images that held the infant's attention the longest were somewhat complex *and* familiar.

This is presented in the following U-Shaped curve on the next page (Pic. 1). Remember when I said Goldilocks had a shape? That shape is the U-shaped curve. Get ready for many more of them.

What are the implications of the novelty/familiarity study? It is well understood that skill development happens when we're able to engage in deep attention. But deep attention seems to have a hardwired backbone of a "just right" relationship between novelty and familiarity. To put it another

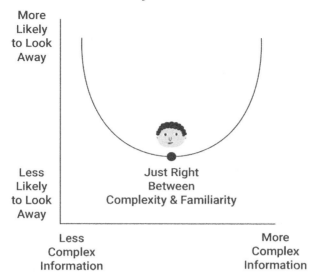

Infant Eye Movements

Pic. 1.

way: when things are too easy, we get bored; when things are too hard, we give up. When we find something somewhat familiar and somewhat challenging, we like it, do it more, and get better at it. This is a topic I'll come back to more when discussing the nebulous idea of self-help in Chapter 9.

Machine Learning and Predictive Analytics: How do machines get "smarter"? Or how do "geeks"—this is a term of endearment—try to get better at predicting the future using numbers? Believe it or not, both of these disciplines are ripe with Goldilocks language and U-Shaped curves like in Pic. 2. (Borne 2016).

Applied to machine learning, researchers have found a just right number of inputs are needed to challenge a learning system but not too much that the system becomes overwhelmed.

Machine Learning and Predictive Analytics

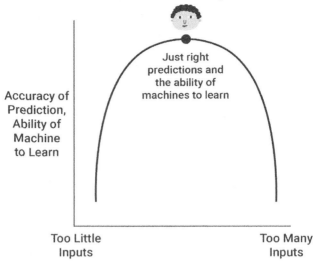

Accuracy of Prediction, Ability of Machine to Learn

Just right predictions and the ability of machines to learn

Too Little Inputs

Too Many Inputs

Pic. 2.

Applied to predictive analytics, data models with too many sets of inputs need to find a "just right" balance of high-quality inputs to maximize outputs.[2]

My take is that when it comes to machine learning, computers may take on the same challenges as humans on this input/output balance needed. I know the human computer analogy is fraught with overreach and oversimplifications, but there are "just right" implications that are worth exploring.

Marriage: Finding just right may be more than just finding Mr. or Ms. Right, at least in regard to making first-time nuptials last. Come to find out, getting married for the first

---

2   This is a gross oversimplification and filled with terms such as convergent and divergent thinking. I'd encourage further research for those interested.

Divorce Rates

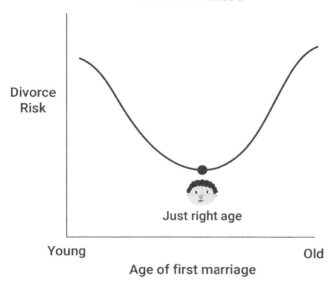

Divorce
Risk

Just right age

Young

Old

Age of first marriage

Pic. 3.

time around the age of thirty seems to be associated with lower divorce rates than getting married at twenty or forty for the first time (Wolfinger 2015).

Is there a just right time in one's life? Hard to say, but the following U-shaped curve in Pic. 3 below shows how this phenomenon shakes out. Don't take this as marriage advice. If you got married at eighteen or fifty-five, this doesn't spell doom. It's just a way of looking at a principle across a broad swath of people.

Growth of Legume Roots: Yes, there is just right in plants! Research has been done showing how legume roots—beans, chickpeas, lentils, peanuts—between plants work better together when a just right amount of signal enzyme—protein messengers—is produced by each of them. This signal protein ensures a vital source of plant protein can go all around. This is one small sign of how coordination works in nature (Aarhus University 2018). This just right in biology and ecosystems is something I'll come back to in Chapters 6 and 10 later on.

Popular Reading: No author has popularized the inverted U-shaped curve more than Malcolm Gladwell. In his book *David and Goliath: Underdogs, Misfits & the Art of Battling Giants*, Gladwell points out how these U curves, in his words, "defy intuitive comprehension" and represent challenges to conventional wisdom and zero-sum thinking. He uses examples such as California's three strike laws and student class sizes to make his inverted U-shape curve point.

The example of student class size is in Pic. 4 below. It shows that a "just right" approach to class size—seems to be around eighteen to twenty-four—may help with the goal of student achievement. This book will not wade into specific policy points, but there may be something to take away a just right approach that can help in these domains.

Classroom Sizes

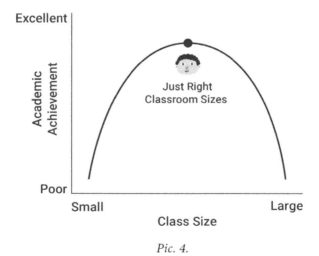

Pic. 4.

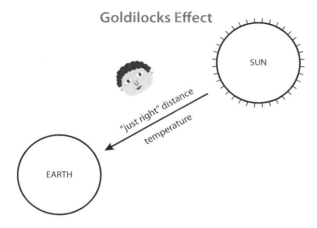

Goldilocks Effect

"just right" distance
temperature

SUN

EARTH

Pic. 5.

Earth Temperature: The "Goldilocks Zone," or habitable zone, is often used to describe conditions needed to keep water a liquid. Being a "just right" distance from the sun allows water to remain in this state, a fundamental feature for life (see Pic. 5). This is a subject I touched on during the introduction. Scientists believe the search for other life forms hinges on the discovery of water in this state. Like the legume example I cited earlier, I'll come back to the subject of the environment later. But appreciating one just right aspect may go far in understanding the implications to our thinking.

It's clear the Goldilocks Principle has been applied to many subjects, but many doubts remain. Scientists often point to things such as bias and correlations or flaws in how research is conducted. They'll also point out nothing in science is ever conclusive or finalized. Sure, baby eye movements, machine learning, legume growth, marriage, water temperature, crime, and class sizes all have some U-shaped curve baked into their understanding. But so what? They aren't directly connected and only share similar patterns and shapes. Many other phenomena take on similar graphical features, and it would be foolish to draw concrete conclusions just from a U-shaped curve.

That is all true. But it's missing the point.

What's connecting all these is meant to represent three big ideas—yes, three!

1. U-shaped curves show a visual just right that often "defy intuitive understanding," as Malcolm Gladwell put it.
2. Just rights are shown by U curves *all around us* in physical sciences (legumes, water, eye movements, machine learning).
3. Just rights are *within us* in social phenomena that we have some agency over (crime, class sizes, marriage).

In the introduction, I shared how my initial relationship to Goldilocks came in the form of the formal and applied sciences. As I've matured, aspects of storytelling have found their way to understanding meaning. This book will be an exploration of both. As I mentioned before, the themes of the book will pull on the tension between ideas.

Much like the car you can't stop seeing, I'm now going to take a journey in three parts. The first part will occupy more of the formal sciences like mathematics and biology. The second part will be an exploration into the applied sciences like economics and psychology. The final section will delve into the existential topics of religion and death. We'll then conclude and summarize the themes and takeaways.

For now, we head off to the human intestinal system. I told you we'd be taking interesting turns, and this one examines a just right baked into our biology and more. Its implications are both big and small. Let's take a closer look at the word guts.

CHAPTER 2

GUTS—A DEEPER LOOK AT A JUST RIGHT WORD

___

Being deeply loved by someone gives you strength, while loving someone deeply gives you courage.

—LAO TZU

I don't know when my love of words with multiple meanings began, but I have a pretty good idea. In the 1985 movie, *Back to the Future,* Marty McFly and Doc Brown get hung up on the word "heavy." Marty, who has just traveled back in time from 1985 to 1955, uses the word "heavy" to note something big and meaningful, specifically how his arrival has disrupted the future marriage of his parents. Marty had used it previously several other times, prompting a bewildered Doc Brown to offer the following retort:

There's that word again. "Heavy." Why are things so heavy in the future? Is there a problem with the Earth's gravitational pull?

It's clear that culture, age, and time travel created a large gap between Doc and Marty. Doc Brown's stiff and awkward qualities didn't help either. Either way, the word highlights what an odd pair they make. The word "heavy" is used as a dialogue device to lend weight—see what I did there?—to their divide.

Another childhood favorite was "burned," or more specifically, "you got burned." No skin was damaged, but it was clear that pride, feelings, and reputation were at stake whenever it came out. It could be heard from the lunch table to the soccer field at recess. Restrictions weren't put on who could say it. It could be uttered by onlookers as well as the person trying to establish a social pecking order. It was also flexible and could be shortened to just "burned!" or "ohhhh burned!" with the same effect.

The reason words and phrases like this "work"—another multiple meaning word!—seems obvious. Burns really hurt! I'm not a linguist, but I imagine this is how language works. Words catch fire—sticking with the burn theme here—in other contexts, and meanings change, even for words that emotionally hurt. Heavy probably worked the same way.

Skip ahead a generation. My son now constantly tells me I got "roasted" when we're playing basketball or video games. Sometimes he substitutes the word "cooked." I'm not sure why. He's also constantly putting me "in the blender." I have to laugh at these trash-talking sessions. What's next? You got seared? Pan-fried? Sautéed? Baked? Steamed? How many cooking phrases are left to co-opt into the world of verbal jousting? He is Marty McFly to my Doc Brown without the time machine.

Where am I going with all this? This chapter is not about slang, linguistics, recess, my son's trash talking, or cooking. It's about how my examining something simple like "heavy" or "burn" reveals something else: curiosity. This chapter will be an exploration in taking things apart as a means of gaining greater "just right" truths. The stakes can be low, like in understanding the relationship between Marty McFly and Doc Brown. Or the stakes can be high, like what we'll see coming up.

This chapter will explore the word guts. The word is important because its four unique meanings have something big to say about searching for "just right." We'll start with storytelling as I introduce you to "Rich." His story offers a lot into the four definitions of the word, how our conventional understanding of its meanings gets off balance, and how examining one twenty-four-hour period in his life is instructive in searching for a more just right. Then we'll dive into what science may tell us about something more fundamental within us. It's strange and cool, much like time travel—at least in theory. Let's get started.

When I met "Rich," I couldn't have imagined someone having a worse five-month period. It was a horror show of misfortune. Its origins may have been his physical gut, but one could argue its beginnings started sooner.

In the beginning, gut pain led him to see a doctor. The doctor told him he had a hernia. Unfortunately, his hernia was cutting off vital blood and nutrients to his small intestine. To make matters work, the same scan that diagnosed his hernia also showed something additionally ominous: a kidney tumor that needed to be removed. Plans were quickly made to fix each problem with surgery.

Just after Rich got home from his hernia/kidney tumor double surgery, he suffered a heart attack. Rich was rushed to the hospital for more surgery, this time on his heart.

Following the heart attack, another stroke of misfortune found him: he developed inflammation around the sac of his heart called pericarditis. He required more tests, more drugs, and a long trip to a rehabilitation facility to recover from these four issues that all happened in quick succession.

With all his own challenges over the past five months, Rich had something else weighing on his gut: the health of his wife.

Prior to his hernia, kidney, and heart events, he'd been the primary caretaker for his wife. Her health had been declining fast, even before his health started to suffer. Fortunately, his children stepped in to care for her while he was in and out of the hospital and rehabilitation.

As he was attempting to recover, it became clear to their family his wife would not. The first time I met him, it had been one week since his wife passed away. The pandemic was also just starting, the unknowns of how to plan around a death at their apex. This was the subtext for our first meeting. I had a feeling it wouldn't begin with a discussion of medications. I didn't have any premonition it would reveal all the meanings of the word guts.

"My wife's funeral is tomorrow," he told me as I asked him the usually innocuous question of how he was doing.

Clearly, we were going to cast aside the "get to know you" pleasantries.

I couldn't tell if he said it because he knew I knew or because he didn't think I knew. Looking back, I think he said it because it was the only conversation he could have at that moment.

"I read about your wife's passing. My deepest condolences. Is there anything you want to talk about today?" was all I could offer.

One secret healthcare clinicians don't like to talk about is their obsession with keeping conversations on track. Or more concretely, *on time*. Focus on the issues, address those issues, and do it efficiently because time is a wasting. Their and my obsession comes from a logical place; there are lots of boxes to check, and sometimes there are consequences if all the boxes aren't checked. They also constantly worry about falling behind. I imagine most people who work in a service industry can relate.

I realized this open-ended question could veer us far off the topic of drugs. My boxes may go unchecked. Yet asking it seemed the only obvious question.

"I want to talk about how I'm going to make it to my wife's funeral tomorrow," he said.

I asked him to explain what he meant.

With a voice made for National Public Radio, he explained how he wasn't able to control his bowel movements since her death. Food was a tricky proposition; he had to be near a toilet to assure he didn't have an "accident." He insisted he wasn't sick.

I went through a checklist of questions with him: no temperature, no more than four loose stools per day, no unusual smells, no weakness, no cough, and no rashes. His gut told him grief was wreaking havoc right now. Somehow, this was how his insides were coping with the sadness.

He went on to explain how the pandemic meant the "funeral" would be outside, next to the gravesite. Six people would attend, which was the maximum allowed at the time: himself, the pastor, a casket carrier, his two children, and a gravedigger. All except him would help carry the casket. No bathroom would be in sight.

"I have to be there, but I don't want an accident out there. What can I do?"

We decided to methodically work through what to do. We adjusted medicines he wasn't taking properly, hoping that may help a bit. We made an emergency plan: a trip to purchase an adult diaper and how to use an over-the-counter medicine called loperamide, which he wasn't familiar with. We discussed the dose with such detail that he set an alarm to take it at just the right moment before he left for the gravesite. He even planned to carry an emergency tablet while helping with the proceedings.

We spent the rest of the meeting on matters of the gut, or maybe the heart. Sometimes one gets conflated with the other, but I'll get to that later. He talked with ease about faith, the future, and how things would be alright in the end.

Regarding that comment about "alright," maybe he was trying to convince me or convince himself. All I can say is that it sounded convincing in the moment. I wasn't sure what the "alright" meant either, but that didn't seem to matter to him as he didn't offer up what he meant. I knew I was just a gut sounding board, my own gut telling me to drop any pretense of being just the drug guy.

Despite all the disorder of the past five months, Rich's mind seemed to be perfectly clear. With everything broken in his gut, his optimism under the circumstances spoke to something right that I was curious about understanding.

There is much to untangle in the twenty-four hours I walked into Rich's life. At its core is the story of guts in all its four meanings. Examining its meanings allows for the curiosity needed to search for a just right understanding.

First, there was the application of a digestive Band-Aid called loperamide, which is a drug that works on the part of the gut that is normally meant to register pain. The irony of giving his grieving intestines a medicine that, in other contexts, numbs things was not lost on me.

Loperamide is a wonder—remember, I'm a pharmacist—because its chemical structure allows the body to keep its activity mostly confined to the gut. This minor modification has major consequences. As a result of this modification, loperamide can be sold over-the-counter (OTC) instead of being restricted. I'll explore even more intestinal searches later in this chapter, but it's important to appreciate the power of science in applying a just right amount of relief.

The second feature of guts was what Rich's funeral attendance represented. In this context, we often use guts interchangeably with words like "important," "critical," or "essential." We realize something fundamental in play, and the word tells us everything about the gravity that the event takes on. Maybe that's why rituals, like funerals, parties, and weddings, tie our guts into knots sometimes. It could be fun, it could be tragic, but we all realize something important is at stake. Like we're getting to the gut of *something* about who we are as people.

Third was how Rich coped and overcame the adversity his body was throwing at him, a virtue that's wrapped in words such as "courage" or "hero." This is something I'll explore later, but it often means something that many people hold with the highest order. It's also a just right that can't be ignored.

The fourth and final feature of guts was Rich's intuition. The "gut" voice inside his head was telling him his ailing gut was connected to grief, not to infection or anything else. This version of guts is an unconscious feeling, a listening to the body's nervous system and seeing what it has to say. Rich was keenly aware of his unconscious and trusted its plan for him.

Remember when Rich and I ran through the battery of questions to make sure his diarrhea wasn't due to an infection? I forgot to mention that he also declined doing the normal battery of stool tests. We talked about the sort of infections he was susceptible to by virtue of being in the hospital in the preceding months. I made sure he knew that. Right or wrong, he was going to let his gut guide his version of truth.

There you have it: Rich's episode with guts is digestion, what's essential, courage, and intuition all happening over one twenty-four-hour period. What became clear is that all of them were supporting him in equal measure like a four-legged stool, an image of which follows in Pic. 6 below. Because of their orientation on the stool, all the legs are dependent on one another to be leveled "just right."

I'll come back to this stool image again. But first, here's an additional reflection on what it means to be curious. Examining Rich got me curious about a word, which then got me curious about the nature of curiosity itself. I know that's a lot of curious!

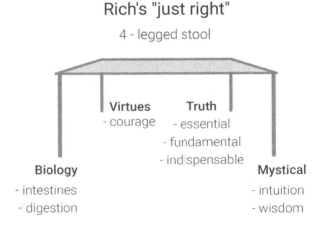

Rich's "just right"
4 - legged stool

Virtues **Truth**
- courage - essential
- fundamental
- indispensable
Biology **Mystical**
- intestines - intuition
- digestion - wisdom

Pic. 6.

First, I started to appreciate that curiosity often comes when nobody is watching, a tough situation when you're stuck at work or school all day. Sure, learning happens there, but curiosity is about desire. How does someone cultivate desire when somebody is demanding something, like an exam or progress report? Beholden to external expectations, curiosity becomes a more difficult impulse to dreg up. Although there are many think pieces asking students and workers to "work in their curiosity zone" and "find curious people to be around," it often comes down to this: be curious about what makes us curious and search for a place to express it.

Getting curious about guts, I started to wonder if some of my blind spots were largely culture. I've historically conflated guts with R-rated movies, R-rated words, John Wayne, Rambo, Marvel superheroes, and stories about overcoming adversity. If I'm prone to a lot of TV and hero worship, doesn't it make sense my stool got lopsided by making the courage leg too big like in Pic. 7 below?

My Misguided Guts "just right"

4 - legged stool

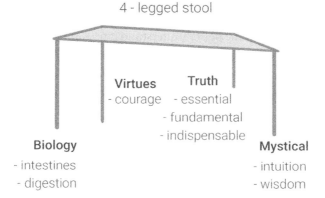

Pic. 7.

Celebrating the virtue and triumph over adversity is important. In a way, it feels very primal, like something right is getting addressed. Rambo always knew the right thing to say and do. The challenge is we never break things down in the spirit of just right understanding. As you can tell, I desire to break words down. The questions for everyone are: What is worth breaking down to find the truth? What's worth being curious about?

The truth of my own life revealed uncomfortable realities. My gut told me I spent too much time trying to satisfy other people's expectations and not examining my own. Put another way, my intuition told me I can be an incurious person in service to other people's needs instead of looking at my own.

But wait, I'm writing a book with a section on curiosity! Isn't that like saying Oprah doesn't think about interview questions? The truth is, I've been ignorant about what makes somebody just right curious: desire and freedom. I think it's why meeting Rich had such an effect on me. He acted with strength and without restraint, like a real-life Rambo but without the guns and body butter.

Before we wrap up and say goodbye to guts, I want to pivot to interesting science that deserves a fresh look. While Rich's story has helped me better understand curiosity and breaking words down, my research also revealed something in our gut that helps break things down. It is the story of a curious and underappreciated carbohydrate called fiber. Let's break it down.

All personal sentiments aside, there must be a better way to understand guts, at least the biological one. While I've gone on about intuition, essential, or courage, breaking down the anatomical reveals some wonderfully right. Appreciating it can help us to better begin to see a just right within and around all of us.

Breaking down the inner—no pun intended—workings of the gut is a book all its own. Here's the most succinct version of the gut I came up with. It also comes with an exciting flourish:

- At least fifteen feet long for most adults (Villines 2021).
- Contains two types of sphincter muscles (Cleveland Clinic 2021).
- Produces seven different digestive juices (enzymes) (Denhard 2022).
- Home to thirty to forty different bacteria living in collaboration with the human body (Beaugerie and Petit 2004).
- Enzymes come from the pancreas and liver.
- Bacteria comes from food, water, and the environment.

Often, they engage in a complex just right, turning sustenance—food—to fuel. The closer one looks at the mechanisms, the more it feels like magic.

Although I could focus on any one of these, fiber is the focus of this intestinal right. First off, fiber is a type of carbohydrate that the body can't digest. Less than 3 percent of Americans receive the recommended minimum adequate intake of fiber—about twenty to forty grams per day (Moshfegh et al. 2005). Our Paleolithic ancestors were thought to receive one hundred grams per day (Blake 2014). Though most carbohydrates are broken down into sugar molecules, fiber cannot be broken down, and instead, it passes through the body undigested. Fiber has many uses for the body, including regulating the body's use of sugars, lowering cholesterol, encouraging a healthy bacterial microbiome, warding off infections, and helping to keep hunger and blood sugar in check. Fiber is most abundantly found in fruits, vegetables, whole grains, legumes, nuts, and seeds. How are we all so wrong about something so right for us?

What fascinates me about fiber is it's a nutrient that the body doesn't even take in. It's an interloper, taking a drive down the intestines without stopping to see what's inside. Its main role is to help find an equilibrium for the place it never sees, to help feed the microbiome, to help move things along for future fertilizer. Biology has a way of revealing just right relationships and gut fiber is one of them, even if the explanation felt like a public service announcement. The next time you pass by foods at the supermarket, take a moment to be curious about the just right all around you.

Having finished the examination on guts, it would be easy to become underwhelmed. Maybe the subject of guts is not inherently interesting and a deeper understanding of one word felt like something a dictionary can do in ten seconds. We can't be curious about all subjects, knowing that desire comes from unexplained places. Sometimes I look at my mix of podcasts on sports, true crime, health, storytelling, and technology, and I ask myself: what do I even like about these things anyway? Such is the nature of curiosity, the process of taking things apart to reveal just right truths.

Curiosity helps in the search for just right. Next, we will examine our own misconceptions in the search of truth. It will take us deep into another subject that may not initially inspire curiosity: numbers. Just like guts, much can be revealed by taking a closer look.

CHAPTER 3

NUMBERS—THE POWER OF TRUTH AND STORYTELLING

———

To become learned, each day add something. To become enlightened, each day drop something.

—LAO TZU

On January 28, 1986, my third-grade classmates and I were led into a common area at our elementary school. We were told to sit down as the TV was immediately turned on. The room was surprisingly quiet. We all looked around, surprised. We were wondering if this was special TV time we weren't told we'd be getting today.

The teachers explained little other than a terrible thing had happened and to be quiet so we could hear the description. As we watched, newscasters talked over the scene of a horrific accident. Over and over, they seemed to show the same thirty-second clip: a space shuttle surging into the bright blue sky with fire shooting out the back as it propelled itself into space (Encyclopedia Britannica Online Ed 2022).

Everything appeared normal until, suddenly, it wasn't. An explosion followed by two plumes suddenly appear, streaking white clouds separating scattershot into the daytime sky. My childhood eyes could not believe what I saw. Was this supposed to happen? Was that an exploding rocket ship? Were all those astronauts dead? The answers to those questions were no, yes, and yes. The *Challenger* spacecraft had crashed. I couldn't believe it.

The following weeks were an introduction to space news like I'd never seen before. It was the first memory of a news story I remember ever following. The hearings were a confusing mix of engineering language that was way over my eight-year-old head. What wasn't complicated to me were the O-rings. Because of the unusual cold launch day, the O-ring seals that separated rocket boosters had broken. This caused burning gas to get into an external fuel tank, resulting in jet fuel becoming bomb fuel. To me, it seemed so strange that small numbers like 0.28-inch O-rings and thirty-six degrees Fahrenheit helped cause a disaster that big. How could that be?

The official summary of the *Challenger* explosion is summarized in the following statement:

> *In view of the findings, the Commission concluded that the cause of the Challenger accident was the failure of the pressure seal in the aft field joint of the right Solid Rocket Motor. The failure was due to a faulty design unacceptably sensitive to a number of factors. These factors were the effects of temperature, physical dimensions, the character of materials, the effects of reusability, processing, and the reaction of the joint to dynamic loading (Woodfill 1989).*

Although there is much speculation on the factors that led up to that January day, it's clear a misunderstanding of small numbers had happened. This was my introduction to the power of numbers.

This chapter is about the misconceptions people make with numbers, a powerful tool that cuts across languages and cultures but doesn't always have the final say. The just right search comes in their human application. Numbers are just another means of—hopefully—finding a deeper clarity and truth. What will be revealed is that numbers are for storytellers and truthtellers. Sometimes those two concepts align, other times, they do not. Searching for "just right" means finding a level of discernment to see the difference. Visually, it looks like the following Venn diagram in Pic 8 below.[3]

Numbers Venn Diagram

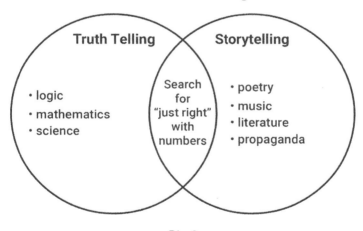

Pic. 8.

Is this too heavy or visual for you? Here's a quote from a smart person.

---

3   Venn diagrams are used to teach elementary set theory, as well as illustrate simple set relationships in probability, logic, statistics, linguistics, and computer science. Many Venn diagrams involve numbers!

"Pure mathematics is, in its way, the poetry of logical ideas."

—ALBERT EINSTEIN

I think Albert would say logic is truth telling, and poetry is storytelling. The truth was the O-rings were not structurally sound, and concerns about their possible compromise were raised prior to the launch (Bektas 2013). The story was that NASA needed the launch from a public relations standpoint due to waning funding and public interest (Teitel 2022).

In its most pure form, truth and story align just right. But in countless other situations, the numbers present imperfect choices where truth and story don't immediately provide clarity. For people like Jim, whom we're about to meet, numbers seem to make things more confusing than clarifying. As he sorts through the numbers, he tries to find where his story and truth align, wading through numbers in search of just right.

"How will I know if this medicine will work for me?"

When I met with Jim, a midfifties male, he had no significant medical issues until recently. He had just developed a heart problem called atrial fibrillation, which is a condition akin to having a musical conductor who's got the band playing too fast for the audience.

It started with a trip to the emergency room (ER). He described a feeling like "his heart beating out of its chest." He was given medicine in the ER in an attempt to control it. While waiting to see if the medicine worked, he had a heart scan to make sure nothing more serious was going on. He then left with a two-week electronic monitor on his chest and medicine to take for at least the next six to twelve months to reduce his risk of blood clots. It was the blood clot medicine that led Jim to seek me out.

Jim got down to business, wanting to understand exactly how this new medicine was going to benefit him.

I went through the details, explaining how blood and its clotting parts can "pool" when the heart is not pumping normally. I drew upon the analogy of how water pools where there is no strong current to push it downstream. A fluttering heart creates less push. Pools collect twigs, rocks, and other debris. Too much debris can cause the stream to be blocked. The human body is no different. He seemed satisfied with the analogy but not with the benefit.

"What assurances do we have that it works?" he asked.

"We have no guarantees it will work," I said. "All we know is it's better than doing nothing. So, we do it. It's also hard to prove something works for any one person when the goal is to prevent something bad from happening. We have to look at many people to show benefit."

He seemed to appreciate my direct honesty. He wasn't done.

"Is there a way to know this is going to work better for me than something else?" he asked.

"Yes, we can compare it to other treatments, and the one you're on is generally safer and more effective," I offered. "But, who it ultimately benefits, and why, can still feel like a medical mystery."

This is a classic healthcare hedge where there are no absolutes.

He shrugged. I could tell the reassurance I was hoping to supply was slipping away. My river and twigs analogy now seemed to be dying. I felt I had no way of getting out of it.

He said he was still open to taking the medicine. He pivoted to wanting to understand how the benefits were measured. Knowing I was already treading water, diving into healthcare statistics seemed like making a murky situation worse. Of course, I didn't feel I had much to lose at this point.

Then, a lightning bolt hit me. I knew Jim was an actuary, a man who looked at populations and used numbers to determine cost and risk, like setting the price on my car insurance. Maybe I could impress him with a number to get him back, to cut through my rocks and twigs analogy from earlier.

I quickly went to the computer and plugged in some numbers. I came out with thirty-nine, a number generated from a statistical measure called number needed to treat (NNT). The absolute benefit was 2.5 percent.

"What's that mean?" he said.

I told him that if we give the medicine he's taking to thirty-nine people, one person will have a major cardiovascular event like a stroke or heart attack prevented after a few years.

"Those odds don't seem so good," he offered.

I imagined to an actuary like Jim, this could mean seeing thirty-nine people with thirty-eight of them standing next to their busted vehicle waiting for an insurance adjuster. I knew that was not how the statistic worked, far from it. But when just beginning to understand numbers, storytelling can fill in the gaps of truth telling. Sometimes I wonder if financial planners see this play out every day when it comes to money.

I didn't know if there was much that I could do to bring Jim back. I tried. I explained when this medicine is taken by thousands of people who have heart rhythm issues, many lives are saved. If you couple that with the approximate 40 percent relative risk benefit carrying over the long-life Jim—presumably—had left, the number needed to treat was just one number helping him make a decision. But once we've attached meaning to a number, it's hard to attach a different one.

Jim said he needed to think about the numbers further. I told him to call me, and he did a couple of weeks later. He continued to take the drug. The comment I made about the percent of relative lifelong benefit finally convinced him. He also mentioned his good insurance coverage.[4]

Hanging up, I started to think about what happens with Jim and all of us in our relationship with numbers. It sent me down a strange path looking at things like trust, homework, and baseball cards. Hopefully, the themes of truth, story, misconceptions, and discernment emerge.

What happened to Jim?

What happened to Jim is what happens to many of us. A dive into the numbers revealed truths that were both confusing and compelling. Numbers can leave us cold, leave us overjoyed, or leave us confused. All realities feel possible. It's a myth that numbers are solid. The truth is that numbers are in the story of the beholder. In Jim's case, it was in the story of a long life he saw for himself and the truth that some benefit, even if small, can be worth it.

To help understand the confusing and compelling, it can help to understand how certain numbers are generated. As we explored in Chapter 2, numbers without curiosity offer little relevance in helping us understand the why.

Take the first number I shared with Jim. First described in 1988, the number needed to treat (NNT) is used by caregivers

---

4   Leave it to an actuary to have good insurance.

to make treatment decisions, especially with medicines (Mendes et al. 2017). The number's size often influences decisions; a high NNT number means a medicine isn't offered. A low NNT number means it is. To make it come alive, it might be best imagined rather than calculated.

Let's say we are really smart doctors who have developed a new procedure for the heart. This procedure requires placing a device into the heart to make it pump better. The improved heart pumping has an absolute benefit of 5 percent at one year of reducing heart attacks. Next, you have twenty people filing into the room. They're all very similar in age and medical history, and they're all told they need this heart pump. If the number needed to treat NNT is twenty, only one of them at years end will receive the heart attack prevention benefit—statistically speaking.

Does this sound confusing? There are even more caveats to the number one. First, we won't know who will receive the benefit because many people may not have a heart attack in that one-year period. Next, we don't know if the twenty-people-group size is statistically large enough to detect any difference. There's another number for that. With all these qualifiers, it can seem like one is the loneliest number.[5]

Statistics aside, the question is knowing how the numbers worked for Jim. Visually, Jim's discernment Venn diagram looks like Pic. 9 on the next page. To understand why Jim took the drug is to begin searching for a just right with numbers.

---

5   *One Is the Loneliest Number* is a song by the rock band Three Dog Night. The song reached number five on the billboard Top 100 in 1969. The band name Three Dog Night is an Australian expression of a cold evening, where three dogs will be close to you if sleeping outdoors. Obscure fact knowledge!

Jim's Venn Diagram

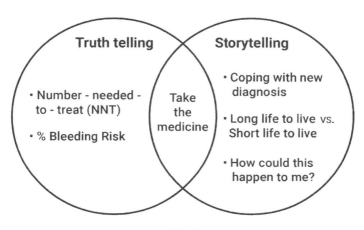

Pic. 9.

Numbers in the context of individual decisions are hard enough, but they can be even more difficult to discern in the aggregate. Numbers have a similar blend of truth telling and storytelling there too. A different type of perspective is needed, even as the stakes take on new meaning. It can reveal itself in something as difficult as attaching a number to a feeling like trust.

Although number truth and storytelling are difficult with health, numbers used in public life can sometimes leave us with a collective confusion. Take this number: a Pew research study in 2019 showed that 70 percent of US adults believe their personal numbers are less secure now than they were five years ago (Orem 2019). Is that seven-in-ten belief perception or actual reality? Is that seven-in-ten a form of truth telling or storytelling?

Here's some more Pew research. Also, in 2019, another survey showed two-thirds of Americans believe made-up news and information create "a great deal of confusion" about the basic facts around current events (Mitchell et al. 2019). How can we get the story straight if our basic understanding of the numbers feels lost? How can we search for just right if truth and story feel so far apart?

One could argue that this is a human problem, not a numbers problem. But if numbers are used as the gateway toward a position, a statement of fact, it seems like all we're left with is something Jim individually used earlier: discernment. It's clear our collective relationship with the numbers is in danger of eroding. Numbers can feel like a gateway to beliefs, not a gateway to facts, but it doesn't have to be that way. Collective discernment is possible.

Although the US numbers show a collective breakdown in trust, or the institutions producing those numbers, other countries do not. In Australia, there is a lot of trust in data. A 2020 survey conducted by the Australian Bureau of Statistics found that 85 percent of the general community trust ABS statistics. The figure is even higher among "informed users," with a near-unanimous 99 percent.

When it comes to trust, the numbers of a story can make it difficult to understand the truth. But the truth is that Australians have a version of trust that Americans do not. Where does a search for just right lie in this situation? It may just be in the simple truth that we can all be fooled when given an incomplete set of numbers. Maybe the decision to have a surgery or take a pill will help us understand this incomplete more. Some numbers are just the start of a process toward wisdom.

What if I told someone they had a 95 percent chance of surviving surgery? Would they do it? Now, the same question posed in a different way: if they were told they have a 5 percent chance of dying from the surgery, would they do it?

As most people can see, these are the same question framed in two different ways. The first question is framed in the strong odds of success, while the other is posed with the real chances of failure. Chances are, if we got two random groups of people together, more people would have surgery with the question posed the first way, and more people would reject it if posed the second. When viewed to the truth and storytelling Venn diagram, using two different numbers leading to two different outcomes isn't hard to believe.

I know I'm not breaking any news. This has been born out in everything from selling toothpaste to recommending medications (Geckoboard 2020). The impact is not trivial. Specific to medications, the difference between telling people a pill will cut their risk of heart attacks by 34 percent results in 90 percent agreeing to take it (Greger 2021). Saying it results in 1.4 percent fewer patients having heart attacks results in only 40 percent taking it. Both are statistically accurate, one using a measure called relative risk and the other using a different measure called absolute risk. This is what happened to Jim earlier. Relative risk meant taking the drug, absolute risk meant confusion on whether it was right for him.

Choosing the way to present numbers can mean everything about whether someone will take a medicine or have a surgery, even if the numbers speak to the same truth. The story we've told ourselves, based on the same pill with different numbers, results in different realities for many. Two truths can result in two stories and a lack of clarity about what's right.

Numbers are a version of truth to human storytellers.

Many questions come from thinking about our relationship to numbers. Is it misleading? Incomplete? Selective? Are we guiding the people to the decision we want? How complicit are we in choosing information that validates our predetermined worldview? Maybe the just right perspective for Americans is to simply start discerning more. Australians are able to do it, and I doubt it has much to do with their numbers/data being objectively safer. Start looking at the story we collectively tell ourselves more and truth in numbers less.

I realize humans have a long way to go in the search for a just right relationship to numbers. I don't have some concrete "do X" or "do Y" plan. Examining the origins of how we got to our perspectives is the theme of this book, a nod to the fact that Jim's Venn diagram is unique. It may not help us solve our collective trust but examining our own number story does help us all build the discernment muscle. Let's look at how many of us sort out the number's world as children: through games and my relation to numbers as finding order.

My love of numbers started when I was nine years old. It first started with baseball, a game I started when the uniform was a T-shirt, shorts, tube socks, and a Cubs hat. My first exposure involved the ball on a tee.

I loved the game of baseball and baseball cards in equal measure. Looking back, baseball cards were a perfect marriage for a kid like me. They gave me an opportunity to lose myself in dreams of athletic greatness and a way to look at numbers to define that greatness.

My draw to baseball was that it seemed to measure everything: how fast the pitcher threw, how far the ball went, how many attempts a hitter had left to get a hit. The bases were numbered. The innings were numbered. Each player on the field even had a designated number. The scoreboard at a major league field was filled with numbers of other games going on. And that's just scratching the surface.

In many ways, my childhood love of baseball numbers feels vindicated. In 2003, Michael Lewis wrote the best-selling book called *Moneyball,* showing how a revolution in the sport could be accomplished by looking at numbers differently. Don't have time to read the book? Go find the movie. It stars Brad Pitt as the lead character Billy Beane.

In hindsight, I think I was drawn to baseball because it represented order. It's the version of numbers as pure truth telling. And the back of a baseball card, just like the numbers on the field, was a way to make sense of that order and truth. Little did I know that debating my friends about who was the better player was a form of storytelling. But don't tell that to twelve-year-old me. I wouldn't have believed it. Blending truth and storytelling with numbers takes time.

They say you really remember your first love of a lot of things. First food, first romantic partner, first family trip. I remember falling in love with the back of baseball cards, where they kept answers my imagination could use. I realize now that my love of numbers on baseball cards fuels my love of sports to this day. It's a just right blend of truth and storytelling where the personal stakes are low, but the feeling of just right is easy to find.

Don't believe twelve-year-old me? How about the story of another twelve-year-old with a similar just right predicament with numbers? When the adult version of truth and storytelling feels stuck, spend time around children as a purified form of reality.

I am often reminded that people do not regard numbers the same way I do. I think this point hits home anytime a parent sits down with their child and looks at their math homework.

My son is twelve years old and in sixth grade. He is articulate, funny, sensitive, and kind. He makes friends easily. He likes sports and video games and likes being dared to do something for money as long as it doesn't involve anybody getting hurt. He also picked up his parents' habits of skeptically questioning everything.

Today's question is about figuring the area of a triangle. I look at the equation to calculate the problem. A wave of nostalgia hits me. Base times height divided by two. I appreciate its elegance and simplicity, how it's a foundational piece of knowledge built into my home, my driveway, and the chair I'm sitting on. I'm getting starry-eyed. He's getting glassy-eyed. It's not like the area of a circle, a beautiful shape reliant on the Archimedes' constant number Pi (Duronio and Hickey 2012). The area of a triangle feels concrete and reliable. The area of a circle is abstract because the number it relies on never ends. To each their own, I guess.

Of course, not everybody shares my opinions on these matters. Especially the one sitting next to me.

"When am I ever going to need to use this?" he spouts.

His head collapses. It's now resting down on his arm on the kitchen table, his floppy hair moving back and forth in a shaking pattern. The story of suffering is real.

"This is pointless! A stupid computer can do it!" he adds.

He then tried to show me a YouTube video of a sixteen-year-old to validate his point. I now understand what the term "influencer" means a little better.

It's becoming very apparent he's old enough now to look at the world and perceive the injustice of it all. He sees education as a torture chamber, an activity with no higher purpose, with children chained to desks when they need to run free.

"What is the point of figuring out the area of a triangle? I'll never have to know that again. How much math do we really need to know to get through our day-to-day life?" he said.

My less-evolved brain wants to come back with some version of either "because I said so," "quit complaining," or "we all had to do it, now you do too." Sometimes those comments win out. But they never solve what lies beneath the childhood despair. The truth is something different.

I answer these are fair questions, especially when someone is trying to make sense of the world. I tell him I probably haven't calculated the area of a triangle in thirty years.

We discuss how much mathematics somebody would need depends on their job. It may be enough to use a cash register. For someone in finance, numbers are driving most of their day-to-day activities.

He says he's already ruled out 99.9 percent of jobs.

I respond that 99.9 percent is a number. I tell him moving through the world of numbers is inevitable. That's the truth. I'm not sure how that's landing with his story.

What I find though, is that my son's discomfort, this resistance as author Steven Pressfield[6] would call it, is my son butting up against the novelty-familiarity concept we

---

6   Read his book *War of Art* if you ever want to do anything creative in your life. You won't regret it.

explored in Chapter 1. The concept is too novel and difficult for him at first. The reaction is to look away.

The easy answer is to say it's pointless and give up. But given the right mentoring and support, the novelty/familiarity U curve can start to move into equilibrium, much like the baby's eyes locking onto something for just a bit longer. The same applies to truth and storytelling. The "I don't need to know this" (storytelling) butts up to the mathematical reality of the chair he's sitting on (truth telling). Searching for just right feels closer when story and truth start to reach an equilibrium.

We do one problem together, with me doing all the work along the way. Next, I ask him to fill in one part of the equation, the one he understands the best. He gains confidence, familiarity just a smidge closer. He then fills in most of the equation on the next problem. After that, he's doing the whole thing. Rinse and repeat. Now it's fun. Novelty is just right. And guess what? The pointless is now an opportunity for high-fives and smiles. Can you believe this chair I'm sitting on!

This is just one moment of many, an example that I did succeed once in helping novelty, familiarity, truth, and story find an equilibrium. When numbers plugged into base times height divided by two make sense, a new truth and story emerge, like sitting comfortably in a chair and typing these words.

The search for just right numbers is a blend of truth and story. Numbers are everywhere, so baked into our everyday experiences that we sometimes forget where truth and story lie. It's in measuring the area of a triangle, looking at the back of a baseball card, calculating the benefit of taking a medicine, a public opinion poll, or a measure of trust in our systems. Big picture, little picture, individual and collective, it feels like the only tool we have is one of discernment.

Mark Twain apparently once said, "Facts are stubborn things, but statistics are pliable." I'm not sure if he actually said that, as a lot of quotes attributed to him are apocryphal, but I think the same thing can be said of numbers. They are pliable. Getting them just right is just hard.

Knowing that numbers are incomplete tools means they can help us color in certain lines but not all of them. For Jim, an absolute benefit of 2.5 percent was unimpressive. A relative benefit of 40 percent was persuasive enough to take a medicine. His story and truth were more in the 40 percent, helping him make a right decision for him.

Numbers set prices and give us a pulse of what a country is thinking. They have the power to change decisions. Being a good steward of that power both in presenting numbers and using the tool of discernment is critical. That feels about as Goldilocks as anything I can say on the subject.

With numbers holding some version of truth, we now transition to a just right search where nothing can feel true but despair. Next, we are going to look at a just right that will look at the role of impermanence on our mental state. Of a search that holds just now with importance, and looks to the power of time, treatment, and self-healing as versions of just right.

CHAPTER 4

MENTAL HEALTH—DARK ALLEYS AND JUST RIGHT HEALING

———

The farther that one goes out (from himself), the less he knows.

—LAO TZU

Watching someone in the depths of mental despair is its own form of misery, like getting hit with projectile sadness. You realize it's an emotional illness that may be heading for you. In those moments, the search for just right feels many miles away. The challenge is the unclear path, both for the person experiencing the suffering and the person trying to help. Sometimes, I find myself as both a witness and a clinician in these situations. Annie was a good example of that.

"I called because I don't know what to do. I'm really struggling right now," she said through tears.

Her voice was immediately familiar. I sat at my desk and rubbed the back of my head, a habit I have when trying to rub some breakthrough idea out of my brain. Somehow, I must think my brain is like a genie bottle. Maybe it's the sensory experience that grounds me, if only for a moment.

I'd been working with Annie for the past six weeks. Her psychiatrist was unsure what to do with her medicines, which led to her seeking another set of eyes. That set of eyes was mine. She'd creep into my thoughts at night, my subconscious working through what to do next. Nobody she worked with had any answers, and I was in the same lot.

I'd only interacted with Annie over a screen and phone. She was in her early thirties, dressed casually from the waist up, polite, and warm. She felt like she was on the cusp of tears at any moment. Her mental health had declined to the point where she wasn't working.

I could get her to smile, but only briefly. She felt like a person hanging on by a string. Being around someone ready to cry is precarious. On the one hand, she needed the emotional outlet. Let it out, don't bottle it in. On the other, any crying episode might require us to stop while she regrouped, as comfort was the only recourse.

I felt I was all comfort and no help. Being in the business of medicines means asking many linear questions. Nothing seemed linear here. I chose my words carefully, hoping to keep the conversation moving.

What I found during our first meeting was baffling. Various doctors had changed nine different medicines in the past two months. This was not medicine; this was someone thrashing about for solutions. All these uncoordinated opinions were not helping.

We talked about alcohol, cigarettes, and street drugs as medicines. I told her that her medicine plan—and who was making it—needed to be simplified. She also needed a captain of the medication ship who was seeing the big picture.

"I can't think right now. I'm too emotional to think. I have no idea what to do here. I just want to make it stop," was all she said.

These declarations punctuated our conversations. I felt she'd hit rock bottom even though I had no way of proving it. I realized it wasn't for me to prove either because only she could answer that for herself.

We discussed a program where other people like her would surround her, where her mental health would be a full-time job, where the decision makers weren't operating in separate silos. I rallied those siloed providers to the idea so they could express a consistent message.

I knew her answers were not at the bottom of a pill bottle. I told her a pill, in a best-case scenario, is a tool to stabilize things so the real work can begin. Finding just right would require her to expand her vision, to thrash about and surrender in equal measure.

There is no rule book on how to help the Annies of the world, no helplessness brain probe to quantify the anguish. I can say this intensity creates an inertia to action, any action, sometimes. Try something—anything. This is why people being treated for the most severe forms of mental illness utter the "I feel like a guinea pig" phrase more than any other I encounter. There is no caregiver playbook on how to respond to these comments. Oftentimes, all I offer is a sense that I'm here and listening. The just right we will explore is often sought in the just now.

Looking across the mental health landscape, there are some encouraging just right signs. Western culture is awash in messages of mental health awareness that didn't exist a generation ago. Commercials, social media posts, and public messages have proliferated to destigmatize what used to live unrecognized in the shadows. Collectively, we seem to inch even closer to recognizing mood disorders as the brain injuries they are, which is a good thing.

Although awareness has improved, tangible mental health solutions have been slower to arrive. The most popular medications used for depression are selective serotonin reuptake inhibitors (SSRIs). As a class, they showed improved symptoms in about 20 percent over a placebo in people with moderate-to-severe depression (InformedHealth.org 2020). In absolute terms, it may mean treating five people so that one gets the benefit. For the most challenging illness, it's where the "guinea pig" comments stem from.

So, what to do? How do we better understand what is going on? Is searching for just right doomed?

To look for just right, understanding where someone like Annie falls on the U-shaped curve can lend some perspective. A typical example follows. Most models explaining mood disorders attempt to represent someone along the U-shaped spectrum. Many can relate to the experience; people fill out a questionnaire aimed at telling doctors where they are prior to their visits. What's happening is an attempt to place an objective number on a subjective experience at a moment in time. They might as well ask: how just right do you feel right now?

Let me be clear. These are moments in time when the middle is not the goal. The search may be in seeing the moment for what it is: a moment on the curve to understand that there's up to be had if low and down to be had if high.

Mental health often combines brain injury with perspective. What is joy without experiencing sadness? Heartache without love? Euphoria without defeat? One helps us better understand and relate to the other. Both are necessary to the human experience. But being able to understand our lives in relationship to the U-shaped curve on the next page (Pic. 10)

Mental Health

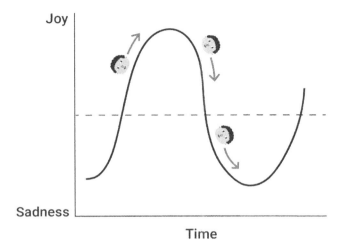

Pic. 10.

can be critical to the ebb and flow time and impermanence offers. It isn't dismissing the sadness or understanding the effectiveness of drugs. I've seen them work. It's understanding that sadness and suffering are part of feeling alive. Sadness can be a form of just right when it isn't turned into dysfunction and distress.

Taking the U-shaped curve further, do we understand what any mental health treatment is really doing? The simple answer: far more than we used to and not near as much as we'd like. What is emerging may help rethink searching for just right.

Let's specifically look at depression. Research into depression shows the hippocampus, found in the mid part of our brain, to be very susceptible to loss in activity when regular sadness sets in. The hippocampus is critical to both memory formation and emotions. It's very active in development during adolescence, which is why our teenage years can seem so vivid, fun, and sometimes fraught when looking back as adults. A lot of firsts happen for the hippocampus during this time. Despite its susceptibility to loss, it's also a brain area known for regrowth.

The scientific term for this regrowth is called neurogenesis, and it's only been recently understood. Medications for depression are thought to affect levels of chemicals like dopamine, norepinephrine, and serotonin. But what they may also be doing in the most sensitive brain areas is supporting the body's cellular repair processes in those most sensitive areas (Julien et al. 2020).

We need to start talking about mental health treatment this way. Any mental health treatment, whether a food, pill, potion, cream, or conversation, is a way to give the body a chance to find its way back to just right for itself. It may not look or have the same outcome for everyone. But for the mystery of sadness, it's important to know its counterpoint joy is within the body's reach.

We can take heed as family and caregivers. Often the distress is so strong, so deep, and so intoxicating that the world can seem smaller. The Annies may never get better. For Annie's loved one, the world can get smaller as well, the projectile sadness leaving its own scars. Searching for just right can take many false turns and end in many dark alleys. It rewards the persistent. The steep just now climb up the U-shaped curve is the only way forward.

The next story about Claire is a bit different, but it speaks to the complexity we all appreciate that goes into mental health. The ingredients are different, but the search for a just right understanding touches on similar themes. Let's meet her.

Claire was a midfifties woman with a raspy voice, and she was casually dressed on the day of our video visit. As soon as she spoke, I realized my focus for meeting with her. Claire smoked a lot—three packs a day.

Claire worked alone at home in IT technical support, allowing her to smoke until her heart's content. With her divorce and her kids now moved out, she admitted she didn't have to pay others much mind. Being alone was nothing new. But the pandemic took her isolation to a new level. Her smoking had made her fearful of going anywhere, thoughts of ravaged COVID-19 lungs weighing on her already emerging shortness of breath. The irony was that the stress made her smoke more. We call these negative feedback loops.

"Something has to be done. I don't have much time," she told me as we started the visit.

I remarked to her how self-aware she was about the stakes involved. She knew this was an inflection point. Young enough to know if she quits now, she may be able to stave off the worst of the lung damage for a time, but old enough to know that any further delay will lead to greater mental and physical suffering. She badly wanted to be a grandmother who would be able to pick up her future grandchildren.

"I know the right thing to do. I just feel powerless over it," she offers.

"I've heard that from others," I tell her. "And we're going to try to find a way to feel some level of control."

She takes a deep breath. She looks a bit sad through the screen.

"I look at the cigarettes sometimes, and I get so disgusted with myself," she says.

"It's understandable you feel that way. But we have to focus on finding a way out," I respond. I sense she can take this level of firm redirection okay.

We talk about triggers, prior attempts to quit, readiness for change, developing a quit plan, support systems to help her quit, and the medicines. It's the standard quit playbook. It's funny when patients realize we've gone fifteen minutes without talking about a single drug. Drugs are my job, after all. But I've learned that the just right search lives in the moments where change could happen. Or understanding the why.

Claire and I start to sound it out. She tells me that smoking is her way of coping with the painful loneliness and self-doubt she experiences. She's trying to find a new job during the pandemic, which is something she hasn't had to do in over twenty years. She can't see her children. She has zero interest in seeing her ex-spouse. She has one close friendship. Her parents have passed, and her siblings are not in close contact. This all adds up to the feeling of being alone. She confides she hasn't touched another human—hug or handshake—in seven months.

This is how I imagine prisoners feeling.

We come up with a plan. We talked again several more times. There is progress and then setbacks. She faithfully uses the nicotine replacement patch. It helps to a degree, and she slowly reduces her cigarette burden. She's on her way as I have her call the nicotine replacement counselors through a free program.

After the cigarettes, we discuss something equally dangerous and ominous. It's not a pill, cookie, or cigarette. It is not a vice in any sense of the word or a thing we normally associate with poor health. Getting her closer to just right means addressing an equally different nemesis on her health that has nothing to do with flesh and bones. It's companionship.

Sometimes we encounter situations where the thing we're tasked with doing aligns with the actual problem—see a flat tire, fix a flat tire. This is why yard work is sometimes satisfying. Other times, the thing we're told to fix is only part of the issue. This is like fixing a leaking pipe only to realize there's water damage or noticing the wheel axle is broken when trying to fix the tire. Claire's situation revealed the water damage or the broken wheel axle. It just took a little more searching.

What was the water damage and wheel axle in Claire's case? Claire was lonely.

One could argue that Claire's cigarette smoking and loneliness are equal in their impact on her health. Here's why: researchers tasked with evaluating loneliness have found that social isolation is associated with serious negative health outcomes, including dementia (50 percent increased risk), heart disease (29 percent increased risk), and stroke (32 percent increased risk). Another study showed a 50 percent increase in premature death, similar to the risks of smoking fifteen cigarettes per day (Morin 2018).

With that in mind, a visual metaphor comes to mind. Searching for just right in mental health means holding these two creators of suffering, the cigarettes and the loneliness, in almost equal measure. And cradling an object with two hands recreates another type of U-shape as shown on the next page (Pic. 11).

If this feels too Pollyanna and quaint, imagine carrying a tape measure and hammer for the drywall or the lift and lug wrench for the tire. Often, the job of cradling something with both arms is handling them gently with care. If the job of a caregiver is to decrease suffering and prolong life, is it my duty to address her self-described loneliness and smoking?

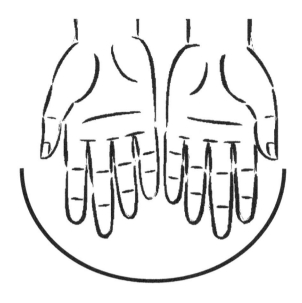

Pic. 11.

What tools are at my discretion? How does a person who deals in hard medical issues handle this matter of the most fundamental of human needs?

Finding a mild ground means holding both things as true and valid, needing time and attention. Getting it just right and giving this person the counsel that she deserves means looking beyond the matter at hand while simultaneously being focused on the directive. It's dizzying, confusing, strange, and feels like the best thing possible. Just right feels like more both/and with less either/or.

I talked to Claire about her social isolation. A pandemic wasn't going to allow me to fix her isolation pain. But I could listen. I could advise. I could implore her to see the risk of the isolation she felt was of a similar health consequence to the object she routinely put up to her lips throughout the day. To hold one is to hold the other. She told me she'd talk to somebody about her loneliness and not keep it inside. I told her that was the best hand she could give herself.

At this point, the next hands I'm going to show are my own. If any just mental health right feels strange sharing, it's my own. Looking back, it had been years in the making. It showed me how the darkness helps me appreciate the light. I only hope I give the people who helped me along the way the credit they deserve.

I showed up at my therapist appointment, not knowing what to expect. I was going to talk about my problems, something I'd told countless other people to do. The space was disorienting for somebody who worked in big medical offices—no waiting room, no receptionist, no hint of antiseptic dispensers. It was just a narrow hallway with doors leading to rooms for CPAs, lawyers, and other therapists. I imagined this was We Work before We Work. You could get your taxes done, settle your divorce, and talk about your problems all in one spot. The combination was hard to ignore; I could imagine people spending a lot of time just in this hallway.

I was invited in and asked to take a seat. My senses were heightened. I was taken by how spare the surroundings were: white walls, Scandinavian chairs, dull colored rugs. There was no hint of anything personal, not even a family photo. The only luxury was the couch—soft and cushiony. The type of couch that says "relax."

I was sitting on a therapist's couch. I thought about all the people who'd probably cried on this couch. I wondered if I was next. I looked at the side table with the tissues and the wastebasket. My engineering mind noted the good decision to put them next to each other. I dug in, resolved not to need those tissues or that wastebasket.

I spent the first three months of therapy in a state of denial. I told my therapist I didn't know why I was there. I resisted sharing anything, even engaging in small talk, which is something I often find uncomfortable doing. To his credit, he could see through my deflection. I imagined he was used to cretins like me hellbent on not cracking. He saw through my tricks of sidestepping and playing nice. I could only keep up the charade for so long. After a while, he began to beat me down. Looking back, I marvel at his patience in sticking with me.

We got into my life. I earnestly tried to show how much I had to be thankful for. Grateful people don't need therapy, right? I told him useless nonsense like how I wanted to look back on my life with accomplishment. He said I was basically full of it, a tough-minded tactic aimed at awakening any emotional state in me. He told me that to truly heal from sadness, it had nothing to do with gratitude or looking at goals. It had to do with the truth. He taught me about the honest reckoning I had to do about my life. And the one truth I'd been looking away from was right in front of me: I'd lived most of my life telling myself how awful a person I was. It was the voice that told me that ending my life seemed like a reasonable solution, even if I didn't act on it.

We examined how all my efforts, all my people pleasing, my affability, my goals, were a smoke screen, mostly to myself. My easygoing nature was a way of soothing the internal monologue that I had on repeat. And that internal monologue was this: I was someone undeserving of love.

I had buried this truth and used all the tools of logic and reasoning as a coping strategy. My search for just right was first acknowledging that. I was overcompensating by using only one part of my brain. To seek just right would require a more integrated approach, one that got me to notice my own emotional signals and to listen to my body, and get clear on what it was saying.

We talked about how it was nobody's fault; assigning blame on anyone or anything was the breeding ground for resentment. He congratulated me on avoiding that nasty trap. I'd get worse, then slowly get better. I went on medication. My doctor knew I was qualified to pick it out for myself with his counsel. We parted ways because he sensed that my recovery was now better served in somebody else's hands. I saw somebody else who helped build on what we started. In time, we realized sustained healing had taken place.

Through it all, I've realized there are silver linings. Searching for just right in myself has made it a lot easier to see the struggle of the people I serve. I can remind myself where I am on the U-shaped curve. It's one moment in time, impermanent by the time I've asked myself where I am on the line.

My own deep sadness made me understand its form of just right in seeing the world. It is realizing where I am at along the ride and knowing I was going to be alright.

Snapshots on the search for a mental health "just right" can feel incomplete. Highlighting one person's experience with depression or loneliness does not even begin to scratch the surface of the complexities. There are policies to be written, facilities to be built, medications to take, studies to be done, and biases to be dismantled. But within all that infrastructure, all those pillars of societal progress lies this: one person talking to another person expressing a suffering that can often go unseen. Take the medicine, get out in the world, find someone with mutual affection to share those times with, and appreciate the joy and sadness.

Seeing that person in three dimensions represents a more self-actualized just right for everyone. Seeing individuals on that U-shaped curve, one moment in time, impermanent, allows for a new perspective. I see it in myself because I've seen it for myself with the people who care about me.

In the next two chapters, I hope to show that while "normal" can feel far away, the pull toward equilibrium isn't far behind. And beyond our best intentions lies forces that put things into balance all around us. I hope everyone continues to follow along.

CHAPTER 5

WITHDRAWAL—A JUST RIGHT FINDING US

———

New beginnings are often disguised as painful endings.

—LAO TZU

Sometimes we are masters of our universe until we aren't. World events happen, tragedies and triumphs unfold, and much of it happens without any say-so from us. We don't make decisions, we don't pick sides, and the only realization is how powerless we are over most of it. Watching or reading the news invokes this feeling in me. But if I said there is a "just right" search in the involuntary way things unfold, could we believe it?

What do I mean by "the involuntary way things unfold"? I'll start by describing an example of what it's not. An aphorism that states "mood follows action" is popular in self-improvement circles. It frames mental health in the doing and well-being where control is king. Whether deciding to take a medicine, prepare a home-cooked meal, call a friend, or go exercise, it's this framing mental health in a doing mindset. It's "just right" where "just us" could be the slogan.

Don't get me wrong. This can be helpful. This is something I'll come back to in Chapters 6 and 9. What will unfold next will not be about choice, action, being master of our universe, or becoming a doomed fatalist. It will be about the reorientation that happens when big or small things happen and realizing there's another reaction on the other side of the action teeter-totter. It's a just right search that explores how events big and small show their reflexive nature. The word reflex will come up often. My hope is it takes on new resonance in the upcoming pages.

Newton's third law of motion is a good example of this reflex in action. Newton showed there are actions and equal and opposite reactions to those actions (The Physics Classroom 2022). Not to see or feel this law is almost impossible. This a bug hitting your windshield, a bird flying, a book sitting on the table, or pushing a friend into a pool. It demonstrates that a balance of force is all around us. Noticing it is a way of seeing the world for what it actually is. Most people—myself included—breezed through this concept in high school. But it explains quite a bit, not just the physics of why bugs go splat on a windshield.[7] It's a just right around us that's everywhere.

Newton's third law also shows up in unexpected ways. Professionally, I see it in people who've undergone chemical withdrawal, which is the focus of the people I'll introduce soon. Observing people's perception of their body's reaction to withdrawal is to appreciate our bodies' lack of interest in picking a side. It's a biologic reaction happening as the result of some chemical action with no apparent master of the universe.

---

7   It's not force, its mass and a bug not being able to withstand the buses acceleration. But you already knew that.

Whether its reaction is equal is something Newton may take issue with, but I hope he'd agree our biology's reflexive aim is at restoring some new version of balance. It may be the difference between a mild pleasure or a tolerable pain, or it may be the difference between just getting by or feelings of utter despair. Either way, our only recourse may be to notice the law as a just right within and all around us.

What will unfold are two stories of chemical withdrawal. To reorient the reflexive nature of things through the lens of what happens when our bodies reorient toward a new equilibrium.

Rob had the look of someone who'd seen hard times. He was in his late forties and was casually dressed when we met before he had major surgery. With any luck and skill, surgery can mean a new beginning. A planned surgery often awakens feelings of fear and hope, and Rob was experiencing both during our sit-down. His experience as a recovering alcoholic showed how reflexive the body can become.

"I'm worried about what these surgery medicines are going to do to me," he said.

This worry led him to his doctor, which prompted his doctor to have him talk to me.

As we talked, I realized Rob was savvy about medications. He understood a drug's effect as a potential friend or foe. During recovery, he'd tried to better understand the wreckage drugs can cause. That knowledge was giving him apprehension about having the surgery at all.

"I don't want any more drugs, but I got to have the surgery to have any chance of feeling better," was how he simply summed it up.

We talked more about his current medications and history. During a discussion about one of his medicines, I found some clarity about another source of his apprehension. After a prior surgery, he'd experienced a drug withdrawal when a muscle relaxant he'd been regularly taking was abruptly stopped just as his body was trying to recover from the procedure. The result was not pretty.

"I felt like I was having a heart attack," was how he described the withdrawal experience.

I noted he'd added a traumatic healthcare experience to his chemical journey. He was on that same muscle relaxant now and was desperate to get off it. He saw no hope, as it significantly improved his quality of life. He also didn't note any side effects. I told him to set aside those plans for now.

We talked about his other fears. He had a big one he wanted to review.

"These opiates, man. I'm worried the next time I take them, they're going to hook me."

I validated his concern. Rob had never abused them and had received them before. I was glad he was keenly aware of their potential grip. His connection to the recovery community would help.

We discussed his prior opiate experiences. He'd never experienced the "rush" he got from booze. I explained that self-awareness was helpful. I explained it would help him understand the difference between his muscle relaxant dependence and alcohol addiction.

We talked some more.

In the end, he made a tentative plan to accept opiates for no longer than forty-eight hours after surgery. I suggested a discussion with his anesthesiologist about local pain-relieving options. I knew they existed for the surgery he was having.

Looking back, Rob's reflex was taking many forms, both emotional and biologic. It included his reflex to look at things through the lens of addiction, the power of an unintentional withdrawal, and what lay ahead. Rob's wariness gave me comfort his outcome may be better than most; on some level, he'd already found a version of the just right search within himself. Newton's law would apply their chemical force, but Rob would apply his own.

What was happening inside Rob? How does his story inform us of the reflexive force of being without? And how does it explain any just right reorientation? What lies beneath this question is of biologic and emotional resonance.

Much was going on biologically. First was Rob's muscle relaxant, tizanidine, a medication that acts on a particular set of cells in the central nervous system. The central nervous system impacts body functions, including heart rate, blood pressure, breathing, and digestion. It springs into action in everything from saving someone from a burning building to making sure the pizza you had for dinner gets turned into energy. Tizanidine attempts to reduce involuntary muscle contractions by decreasing the number of false signals that get to the muscles and wreak havoc. He took the medication at regular times and, as a result, established a new spasm balance, albeit one built on increasing doses as tolerance developed. When he didn't take it, a new uncomfortable and traumatizing reflexive process sprang up.

His former challenge of alcohol is a different story. Current research on the dynamics of alcohol in the brain shows its effects to be a mix of multi-receptor activity that both excites and depresses the central nervous system (Julien et al. 2020).

Most can intuitively relate to this on a personal or observational level. It explains why Uncle Larry was mean and mad when drinking while Aunt Suzy was mellow and fun. No two brains are alike, and context means everything. Alcohol is the Magic 8-Ball drug. Shake it up and see what happens. Graphically, Rob's situation may look like the following U-shaped curve below in Pic. 12. Introduce a drug, and with use over time, a tolerance develops, a higher and higher dose needed to establish a new equilibrium. The higher the dose and more chronic the use, the greater the tolerance dip that develops. What happens when that medication is stopped? An equal and opposite reflexive withdrawal.

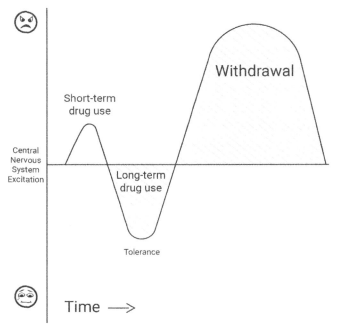

Pic. 12.

In Rob's case, when his tizanidine was accidentally stopped, his motor nerves—the ones that control muscle contractions—were now allowed to repeatedly send false signals. This unimpeded state results in feeling like one is in a burning building or a lion's den, except there are no flames or big cats.

Examples like this are not just confined to muscle relaxants or alcohol. A stroll into any bookstore reveals tales of people withdrawing from tranquilizers, stimulants, and antidepressants, many with tragic consequences. And the memories of these experiences leave their own trauma, like they did with Rob, a reflexive biologic response we were discussing together.

Rob's surgical fear is another action/reaction equilibrium to consider. It's true that surgery for former addicts can feel like shaking a Magic 8 Ball. Despite reassurance, Rob had a reason to be worried: roughly 80 percent of patients undergoing surgery receive an opiate at some point. Data suggests 6 to 7 percent of patients exposed to an opiate run the risk of being "persistent" opiate users after surgery (Lawal et al. 2020). This puts an estimated 5.7 million surgical patients in the US at risk per year. Individuals with prolonged opioid use after surgery constitute a group with potentially significant risk of chronic use. So do former addicts.

Searching for just right may be reorienting ourselves to understanding the risk and settling into the notion that there are involuntary forces beyond our control requiring a conscious reaction to any drug action. Fortunately, in Rob's case, he was applying the reaction so plans could be made to minimize his risk. Rob couldn't totally address the involuntary reflex, but he could apply an action of his own.

If withdrawal is the body's search for balance, it makes sense suffering is involved. But not all withdrawal is the same. Where Rob suffered the immediate version of suffering, there are many others: the headache from one extra drink the night before, trying to get to sleep after eating a plate of brownies, or an unexpected romantic breakup. Withdrawal in this context is the teeter-tooter moving slowly; the actions and reactions are harder to consciously note. The adaptive processes are more insidious, but they are no less destructive.

Brian is a good example. Born with a rare genetic condition, he suffered periods of debilitating pain followed by some level of discomfort his entire life. He described very few moments that weren't clouded by some level of suffering, even on his wedding day or with the birth of his children. Now middle-aged, I sensed resignation and hopelessness were his constant companions. This was his life.

We met and talked about drugs. Because of his condition, he'd been given all sorts of powerful treatments as a young person to limit his suffering. The doses had been escalated over the years leading to tolerance. This also led to a paradox; although he suffered less, the medicines had blunted any experience of pleasure. He wasn't seeking any version of just right. Instead, he was trapped in a feeling of just numb.

He experienced this numbness, this sense of "is this all there's going to be?" sometimes as an intense sadness. He was also made aware that the medicines put his body in a dangerous state. He'd experienced crippling withdrawals in the past when he'd run out of medicine for one reason or another. This led to moments where taking his own life seemed reasonable. He'd seen others do it. Why not him?

Plans were made to wean down these powerful treatments. He'd try, but progress—pardon the pun—was painfully slow.

"I don't think my doctors understand that I'm never going to be able to get off some of this stuff," he'd said to me more than once. After all these years, he was honest about not feeling heard or even being a partner in his care.

I agreed with him. He and I shared the same goal of finding a little less numbness, bit by bit. It would take time. Just having that perspective would give him feelings of hope. Those glimmers of hope were a sign the search was alive.

"What else can I take?" he asked me at one point.

We talked about him sounding like someone who may want to chemically cope. He said he didn't intend it that way. I shared my worry that I wouldn't want him trading one problem for another.

In the end, we talked about cannabis. He was interested. I was a bit apprehensive but open.

We reviewed the pharmacologic pathway as a new brain frontier for him. It could be filled with more numbness, but it may also be filled with more hope. A path toward getting off medicines we know didn't work. We decided to work with a pain provider who'd help him safely start the treatment.

Brian's transition to cannabis had a somewhat happy ending. He started the treatment, and while not perfect, it improved his quality of life. I'd heard from another caregiver later that he felt a little less numb. I had the reflexive feeling that it was the best response either he or I could have imagined.

What's the difference between Brian and Rob? On the surface, not much. They were both middle-aged males who were dependent on chemicals to cope with their day-to-day suffering. Both have been traumatized by their bodies, both chronically and acutely. Both feel trapped: they'd like to not need medicines but feel no other option exists.

But Brian and Rob are different in very critical ways.

In the book *Dopamine Nation,* author and psychiatrist Anna Lembke explores the distinctions between pleasure and pain, both in the science of the chemical dopamine and how it manifests in her patients. Many of these distinctions help us understand withdrawal.

Dr. Lembke outlines how an adaptation in the brain develops when we repeatedly expose ourselves to any pleasurable thing, whether that's a drug, food, or experience. She also outlines the "powerful self-regulating mechanisms" that exist between pleasure and pain, explaining that pleasure and pain are "processed in overlapping brain regions" and "work like a balance." What's more, they are automatic with "no active will" involved, "like a reflex."

If the balance between pleasure and pain is automatic or reflexive, it also has implications for withdrawal. If withdrawal is just a reflex, it is a powerful signal toward this equal and opposite reaction, a search for a just right. Similar to the tolerance/withdrawal curve we looked at earlier, a pleasure pain U- shaped curve in Pic. 13 on the top of page 87 helps to further see the dynamic on a spectrum (Mulder 2022). Anybody who's eaten too much cake at a birthday party or scrolled too much on social media has lived some form of this signal.

Brian had spent a lifetime being given prescription drugs. He was medicated to the point where the distinction between

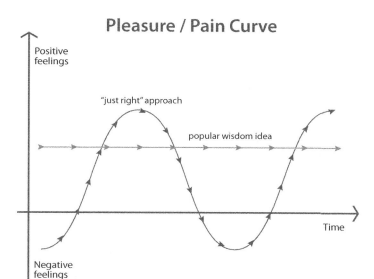

Pleasure / Pain Curve

Positive feelings

"just right" approach

popular wisdom idea

Time

Negative feelings

Pic. 13.

pleasure and pain seemed nonexistent. Rob had spent some of his adult life with substance abuse issues but had shown a propensity to sustain abstinence by choice. Brian's diffuse chronic pain took on a different characteristic than Rob's more localized challenges. All these subtitles matter.

But maybe the search for Rob and Brian isn't about hope. It's understanding rare genetic conditions need rare turns toward reimagining what the just right search means on their terms. The reflexes don't work in a clean, binary way. The equal and opposite reactions are happening outside of an experimental vacuum. Our response to Rob and Brian is to use the science of reflexes as guideposts, not as gospel.

Applying Newton's third law looks more like a day-to-day scalpel within us, even as it can act like a sledgehammer around us. Withdrawal is a just right signal to be recognized for the action and reaction that it is. Where our involuntary reflexes take us is important. Drugs or no drugs, I know it forced me to look at my own involuntary reflexes closer.

I've heard it said that nature loads the gun and nurture pulls the trigger. If that's the case, then my gun has been loaded toward withdrawal avoidance, to live with small pleasures to avoid big pains. It's better to experience small actions with little pleasure than develop big pains with big consequences. For me, this has meant a life of risk avoidance.

This is not to say I haven't taken chances. I've moved away to school, changed jobs, changed schools, and gotten in and out of relationships. At the time, all these things created big reactions in my life. Maybe even a withdrawal of sorts for what I was leaving behind. But the fear response has always kept me from taking the biggest swings.

This has manifested in countless childhood examples: making sure I had mastered the lessons before heading down the ski hill, taking my training as an elementary safety guard seriously, making sure we were a safe distance away from the self-made firecracker explosion we were concocting. Some people may call that smart, but others may call it cautious. My friends called me a wuss and a dork. All of them feel accurate.

Caution has always meant safety; I've broken bones and received my share of stitches by searching for my edge. My orientation to avoid withdrawal has allowed me to avoid some self-inflicted wounds, but it has not allowed me to avoid deep pain. This is something I'll explore deeper in Chapter 12. As I've tried to make clear, we don't get to avoid some reactions. The reflex reaction will find us.

Withdrawal is a complex topic that is broad in its implications. It manifests in decisions that are big and small. It's as big as an alcoholic who is delirious after suddenly stopping consumption and as small as a stomachache from eating too much ice cream. We have all felt these action/reactions at some point.

For some people reading, it may bring up some big questions: so, what? What's the big deal? What if I know the loss will cause pain? Just avoid the painful thing. Those who don't *do* the thing don't suffer the consequences *from* the thing. Yes, and yet there are millions of alcoholics who suffer and individuals with unfortunate genetic fates who would not see it the same way. Being dismissive or avoidant of suffering does not make anyone immune. Involuntary reflexes and Newton's third law don't have feelings and opinions. Reflexes seek us. We don't have to go to find them.

Recognizing the action/reaction teeter-totter helping us orient toward just right is critical. It's also reassuring and helpful in aiding ourselves and one another in the search. As we've already shown, these teeter-totters operate on a playground, not in a vacuum.

Next, we turn our attention to a subject similar to actions and reactions as we look at intentions and the random order of things. Much like seeing that reflexes don't have opinions, operating in a space where control isn't or isn't an option is a search for just right many find ourselves on. Let's take a look at where the search now takes us.

CHAPTER 6

HEAD AND HEART—SORTING OUT INTENTIONS WITH THE RANDOM

———

A good traveler has no fixed plans and is not intent on arriving.

—LAO TZU

Have you ever listened closely to a graduation speech? I've sat through my fair share of them over the years. For the rare person who hasn't, there are thousands available on YouTube, some with tens of millions of views. There's definitely a market for them.[8]

Some are funny, some are boring, some are inspirational, but all are built on a big idea: intention.[9]

Many of the speeches generally have three acts: we—with assist from family—got ourselves here (the past), we've now done it (present), and now we carry ourselves into the big unknown (the future). They are the types of speeches that

---

8   I'm a sucker for a few of them, especially if they're celebrities. I don't feel shame about it.

9   I did not watch every YouTube graduation video; I'm making an intuitive leap. You'll just have to trust me on this one.

elevate a life to a curated set of controlled choices. It's the "master of the universe" or "mood follows action" mindset we just explored in Chapter 4. This all makes senses: much choosing and control *were* involved in the person listening at that moment. Plus, who wants to listen to a speech that says it was all just an involuntary reflex and luck?

This chapter will explore the tension between action and fate. The first is curated through control, intentions, and choice. The second explores how fate intersects with what feels random or what is often seen as luck. Searching for "just right" is understanding the tension between these concepts.

Let's meet Gus, a person who had plans for a restful sleep and every intention of making it happen. Unfortunately, his body had different plans for him.

I met Gus—a man in his early sixties, big midsection, gregarious, and opinionated—at the medical clinic a while back. He came to me by way of his primary care doctor. He works in customer service, and he is hard to keep on topic, but we got along from the start.

"I got to fix my sleep; it's driving me crazy. You got to help me," was his first sentence.

At least he was clear from the get-go. Sometimes people meet me with no intentions other than "help!"

The first twenty minutes of our meeting was "the world according to Gus."

I've learned that sometimes the way to rapport is by simply pulling up a chair. Maybe he knows I won't challenge his opinions on the world because I'm just the drug guy. My job is his health, not his politics. He seems eager for an audience, so I indulge him for a bit.

Eventually, I get him on track, reminding him why we are here: to reduce the five different sleeping pills he's taking while still not getting good sleep.

I try to untangle how he got here and find it a mystery. He's a good storyteller but not much of a historian. He says he hasn't been able to sleep for as long as he can remember. Medicine on top of medicine just starts to happen. I've heard many versions of "I don't know how I got here" from other people.[10] I think everyone can relate, except Gus's version leaves more for storytelling, even as he's attempting a version of truth.

He announces his fear of going off one particular sleep medicine, clonazepam. He says he's been to the ER three times due to stopping it because the withdrawal symptoms were so severe he thought he was having a heart attack (see Rob from Chapter 5). He says it set his insomnia symptoms back "years." I suspect the fear of being without this medication has instilled the same level of fear as the medicine itself. He now says he violently shakes any time he tries to take any less clonazepam than he takes now.

So, drug guy, what can we do? Help!

We decide to take a "one drug at a time" approach. We agree to ignore the other four sleep medications he's taking for now. Their impact is smaller, and the clonazepam has effects that are both physical and psychological.

I like Gus because he's earnest in getting off the medicine. We set a course, this time tapering off the medicine slower and less abrupt than before. I counsel him on the intention

---

10   This makes me think of a song by the band Talking Heads called *Once in a Lifetime* and you need to stop reading and listen to this song if you haven't heard it.

of being in this for the long haul. He's a willing participant. Each of our follow-ups are crisp. Gus shares details of what he did, when he did it, and the end result. He surprises me. The storyteller and shaky historian is a very good goal setter.

We reviewed what to expect, that clonazepam tapers don't have firm rules, just guidelines requiring frequent check-ins to assess readiness to go down on the dose. We work through lifestyle specifics; he works late, so we set an intention of eating less before he goes to bed. He monitors his bedroom temperature and light, even telling me he increased the thread count of his bed sheets for maximum comfort. He is a man in search of his sleep muse. I'll never know how he got here, but he is intent on where he's going.

After a few months, Gus was able to get off clonazepam. His sleep wasn't much better, but he finally agreed to a formal sleep evaluation, something I pleaded with him that he needed. Looking back, Gus offered me a lesson in the tension between intentions and the seemingly random circumstances we find ourselves in. It made me look at choice and fate differently; they seem both miles apart and inextricably close together.

Gus's predicament speaks to the intentions and randomness sleep can bring, especially as we age. Many of us can relate. Up to seventy million Americans every year will suffer from some form of insomnia, some lasting years. Insomnia symptoms occur in approximately 33 to 50 percent of the adult population at some point in their lives. Chronic Insomnia disorders—commonly defined as at least three nights a week for three months or more—are estimated at 10 to 15 percent (Cleveland Clinic 2020).

The challenges of good sleep can be multifaceted. One is the increasing difficulties that seem to come with aging, a sign of an overall body decline. Sleep efficiency—commonly defined as the ratio between the time a person spends asleep and the total time dedicated to sleep—declines with age, from about 95 percent as a teenager to below 70 to 80 percent as we reach our eighties (Walker 2017). A reduction of one-to-two hours might not sound like much, but it adds up over time. Gus's predicament was complicated by age, something no intention will ever change.

Being overweight is also a factor. About 40 percent of obese individuals have a condition called sleep apnea, which is when the airway is periodically blocked throughout the night. A similar statistic showed that about 70 percent of people with sleep apnea are overweight (Wolk et al. 2003). Gus shared his intentions of losing weight throughout his life. Unfortunately, those intentions never found action. Even if we didn't have proof, there was nothing random about Gus's chances being higher.

Mental health, something I touched on earlier in the book, also leaves us more vulnerable to insomnia. Many of the same regions of the brain impacted by mood disorders, from depression to bipolar disorder, are also involved in sleep regulation (Walker 2017). Even if someone is fortunate enough to avoid chronic mental illness, most can relate to increases in irritability even one poor night of sleep brings. For Gus, we discussed the catch-22 he was in. His sleep impacted his mood, which then impacted his sleep. It's a feedback loop where the only intention we sometimes have is to go after the most likely source. With an almost one-in-two chance he had sleep apnea—Gus was morbidly obese—addressing his sleep made more sense.

Also in the mix is the ruminating mind. I've had many insomniacs lament some version of "I can't shut my mind off" when their head hits the pillow. Comparing our brain to something like a household appliance is inaccurate, but I get the point. There's a mental wind down that feels necessary but out of someone's control. In many ways, it's the perfect intersection of what feels random but where intentions matter. Setting nighttime rituals is critical. The challenge is often the effort involved.

What options do we have for this mental wind down? Over the years, Gus was offered and chose sleeping pills. He's not alone. According to Matthew Walkers' book *Why We Sleep*, about ten million people in the past month took some type of sleep aide. That probably doesn't even account for the individuals who seek out cannabis, supplements, or alcohol for their own DIY remedy. This chemical coping has a number of outcomes. It leads to madness for some, a feeling of respite for another, or a badge of honor for those who brag they only need four hours to get a good night's sleep. I've heard them all.

Whatever their perception, the evidence on sleeping pills for sustained benefit is relatively small and of questionable importance. Whatever just right looks like, looking for the sleep solution at the bottom of a pill bottle, however intentional, may not be the long-term intention we need.[11]

Another option, assuming we don't have other physical or hormonal challenges, may mean placing a just right effort on its importance. The literature is clear that the more time inten-

---

11 I've had many people swear their sleeping pills are the only things that work for them. As long as the risks are clear and they understand the other options, I won't challenge their assessment. They've found this intention to work for them.

sive cognitive behavior therapy may be a great option (Walker 2017). Its intention on steroids, where the act of looking at the smallest details may help further eliminate what feels random.

Looking at Gus closer and understanding the science, I couldn't help looking at the pull between intentions and what feels random in myself. It's easy to see myself in the people I meet. It's harder to find my way out of the predicaments they find themselves in.

I'm not sure when my struggles with sleep began. Some challenges seem insidious, a fog of the aging process. I'm confident becoming a parent didn't help, the multiple awakenings hardwiring some type of middle of the night bell that rings with little hope of stopping. There was also the clock watching, the worry, the mind working through a problem, the hope of getting back to that magic dream. Whatever its origins, it's a struggle to find the right relationship with the simple act of closing my eyes and sitting still. Seeing people struggle with sleep has made me more intentional of my own, an attempt to try and master my own sleep universe.

As Matthew Walker's statistics point out, it's not hard to find a sleep deprived tribe. A fifteen-minute online search is all that's needed to find brilliant insomniac descriptions (Zapata 2021). Although their senses may be dulled by the deprivation, its victims can find moments of clarity, nonetheless. Here are a few:

What do I long for? I ask myself this question in the witching hours because it cannot be asked by day. On certain turbulent nights, this longing is so deep and bald it swallows up the world. Defying comprehension, it just is. I am a black hole, void of substance, greedy with yearning. To be without sleep is to want and to be found wanting.—Marina Benjamin, *"Insomnia"*

Too poetic for you? Other descriptions feel more like blunt instruments:

For there is nothing quite so terror-inducing as the loss of sleep. It creates phantoms and doubts, causes one to question one's own abilities and judgment, and, over time, dismantles, from within, the body.—Charlie Huston

Too morbid for you? Other descriptions get straight to the point:

I find the nights long, for I sleep but little, and think much.—Charles Dickens

What Benjamin, Huston, and Dickens have in common, other than their ability to turn a phrase, is despair in something so many people take for granted. When something debilitating like insomnia happens, it feels like chance has dealt us a bad hand. If we're smart, we get on with the intention of trying to make it right, like Gus's fussing over the light, heat, and thread count of his sheets. And what about that word "try"? The cruelness of insomnia is in the paradox; the harder I "try" in any conventional sense, the worse it can become.

How about one more quote for you from the *Star Wars* films:

Do. Or do not. There is no try.—Yoda, *The Empire Strikes Back*

I know Yoda is a fictional nine-hundred-year-old green creature, but he's right—plus, to get to nine hundred, he probably slept well. It leaves a cruel question: what is one to do if there is no try?

If Yoda was Gus's sleep doctor, I think he'd say that light, heat, and thread count are the "do" that preceding the surrender.[12] For me, it's bedtime reminders on my phone, drinking some tea after supper, shutting the TV off one hour before bed, putting on a sleep story, or starting some intentional breathing. Then it's up to fate to decide.

All sleep quotes aside, exploring what seems random is important. Evaluating the random conjures up the word luck, and viewed the wrong way, luck breeds envy and jealousy. Conversely, luck viewed positively can inspire curiosity and joy. Let's meet Marilyn, who inspired in me a fresh look at a good fortune version of luck. She struck me as a perfect person who was not all that fortunate until she was.

I don't consider myself a superstitious person, until I find myself doing superstitious things. It seems random to think unwashed socks before a sporting event would have any impact other than smelly feet. But once the mind decides it matters, it seems like the best intention is to go with it, or throw the socks in the wash after a bad game.

Most can relate to this in the throes of competition, but I doubt many think about superstitions in the course of their day-to-day work. Superstitions enter into my professional

---

12   Or rather "surrender with light and heat do follow" would probably be the way he'd say it.

life when I meet individuals who seem more like cats than humans, an intersection of random and fate. Let me explain. Legend has it that cats have six lives in Arab and Spanish cultures due to the number six being associated with good luck (Osborne 2021). When I was growing up, nine lives were the standard. The number nine has biblical Judeo-Christian and Egyptian mythological origins, which might explain my understanding. It seems the number of lives assigned to a cat is steeped in stories and legends. I realize the just right cat number can be different, but the sentiment of superstitious resilience is not. Humans believe in something resembling luck, fate, and fortune, which is probably not random.

Marilyn fits my understanding of a resilient cat. Reading about Marilyn and meeting Marilyn were equally marvelous. Her medical record read of a fighter: attempts to quit smoking, heart disease, ten hospitalizations in the past five years, and rehab stays. She had spent a lot of time under medical supervision dating back twenty years.

The artery and venous system are estimated to be around sixty-thousand miles long in a typical human body (Cleveland Clinic 2019). For comparison, the US interstate system clocks in at 46,876 miles (US Department of Transportation 2021). That's a lot of potential road construction. Marilyn had reconstruction on the most critical junctures of that vast system. This was all in service to keeping critical nutrients flowing to her brain and body. My initial assessment in meeting her was this cat had a very good construction crew.

Marilyn was clearly "alive" into her early eighties, and "thriving" was what I thought she was. Her mind appeared sharp. She was quick-witted. She was a good medical historian, at least with the big things. My mind imaged her writing birthday cards, organizing bridge clubs, fussing over her husband, and trips out to the store for supplies. I marveled at her resiliency. I wished for some of her fortitude myself. I wanted to ask if she owned a cat.

"I keep having these pains in my chest when I overdo it," she said.

This wasn't a new complaint. It was something she was trying on a new person.

"Is there anything that makes it better or worse?"

"Housework, in particular vacuuming. It's been going on for a while. My doctors know about it. I don't think there's much they can do about it at this point. I rest and it gets better."

We talked about her smoking habit. She'd only recently been able to quit. She lamented at the suffering it had caused her and others. She also resigned herself that there was nothing she can do at this point. While it may have weighed on her mind, it didn't seem to affect her spirit.

Most of our visit was spent on the chest pain, what the medicines did to take work off the heart, making sure she was following up with her heart team, and improving her blood pressure. We talked about sodium, proper blood pressure measuring, and what to expect from nitroglycerin. We followed up a couple of times. Then I released her back to her doctors. Each of our visits left me dumbfounded.

Was her attitude and spirit the cat with nine lives, or was it her good fortune and fate? Or maybe it was simply the by-product of good care and good luck, a maligned system— sorry Walter Cronkite—giving a woman extra opportunities she may have not otherwise had. Maybe it was both. Whatever it was, it was a success story. A woman who had come out the other side, who'd maybe worn the right socks and never bothered washing them.

It's easy to feel joy rather than jealousy around Marilyn. There is nothing random or superstitious about the good feelings that come from being around good people. All feelings aside, it's helpful to examine the intentions that make any hint of Marilyn the cat even possible.

Marilyn's blood pressure is elusive because its impact is often insidious. It's baked into the background of life. Treating it is filled with all sorts of feelings including: why make the effort to try? What makes taking this pill, putting away the salt, hopping on the bike, pumping up the blood pressure cuff, or shopping the edges of the grocery store worth it?

Most can appreciate that blood pressure is not a trivial concern. Hypertension kills more people than any other condition (Resolve to Save Lives 2022). Approximately ten million people die from hypertension each year, which is more than from all infectious diseases combined. Reducing blood pressure prevents stroke, heart attack, kidney damage, and other health problems. It's often called the gateway health concern and "silent killer" because we often don't feel it until something big happens. Who develops it is driven by intention—high salt, low activity, obesity, family history—and random—genetics, family history.

Sometimes, examples help us understand the distinction. A thirty-five-year-old with hypertension who doesn't smoke, have diabetes, or a preexisting heart condition may have a one-in-two-hundred chance in ten years of starting down Marilyn's path. That sounds like something to put off or an opportunity to act to reduce our reliance on being a cat.

A sixty-five-year-old with hypertension who smokes, doesn't have diabetes, and has some heart disease may have a one-in-eight chance in ten years of ending up like Marilyn.

Is that something to put off? It may seem urgent to some, but there is also a seven-in-eight chance of nothing happening, a reframing concept we explored in Chapter 3. Danger can feel like it's in the eyes of the beholder or maybe the curator of the numbers. Numbers help us find a just right threshold when random spills over to intention, before it's too late.

Looking at blood pressure visually helps us better understand what's going on, a U-shaped curve (see Pic. 14 below) that looks a little more like a J follows (Kulkarni et al. 2020). Come to find out, there is something close to a just right zone (120/80) or at least a "just enough" zone.

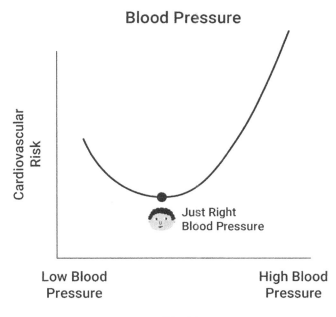

Pic. 14.

For Marilyn, her blood pressure was good enough to get her to the next bridge club or fuss over her grandchildren. The cigarettes that had plagued her until recently were something different. That struggle involved Marilyn's body coming to grips with the most potent of drugs: nicotine. Nicotine is full of intentions, the main one being to give the body more nicotine. It affects the central and peripheral nervous system, activating acetylcholine receptors named nicotinic receptors. Nicotine is so notorious I think they decided to name the receptors after the drug. Every surface on the body absorbs it. It saturates receptors almost immediately upon contact.

Its action in the body seems almost perfectly designed for immediate dependence; it heads straight for the areas of the brain most associated with reward. First, it increases dopamine, serotonin, and glutamate levels. Almost as a cruel kicker, it then blocks the release of a chemical called GABA that is designed to lower dopamine levels. The receptors quickly become desensitized. The high is lost and tolerance develops. But as the person goes to bed, the body resets and the craving can start again in earnest. The person wakes up in withdrawal, that first cigarette a sweet release from the desire trap set by the drug. The process is then allowed to repeat over and over until the cycle is broken.

Breaking nicotine's spell in smoking is difficult. Traditional methods, like counseling, show effectiveness rates closer to 5 percent at six months. Nicotine replacement is a little better at 10 to 15 percent. Medicines like bupropion and varenicline are best at 20 to 25 percent. This means that it may take ten to twenty patients for an intervention, be it a medicine or discussion, to "stick" to the point of success, and that's only at six or twelve months. They have a whole lifetime to restart and many people do years or decades later. Deciding to quit smoking is an intention on overdrive over a lifetime.

For Marilyn, hearing her talk about her busy schedule made it easy to see she had an intention worth living for. Something more mysterious gave her the additional chances to pursue that intention. Whatever it was, it was a joy to watch someone who wasn't squandering her cat lady life.

Up to this point, the search for just right has taken on a number of themes. This chapter looked at the intersection of action and choice as we explored Gus's sleep problems and Marilyn's blood pressure and smoking. They offered opportunities to understand the push and pull between choice, intention, fate, and luck. It underscores the power, relationship, and limits to control, a theme that will continue in what's to come. As Yoda said, our imperative to "do." After that, it's up to forces beyond our control to intervene.

Our next stop is going to be looking at the world of finance, where some of these same choice themes will arise but with some twists. We'll examine the tension behind underlying truths and who profits from understanding them. It will be filled with mystery, some of which will be revealed!

PART 2

HOW WE GOT HERE: WHAT DO THE SOCIAL SCIENCES HAVE TO SAY ABOUT SEARCHING FOR GOLDILOCKS?

CHAPTER 7

ECONOMICS—A JUST RIGHT UNDERSTANDING OF MONEY, MOTIVATION, MYSTERY, AND MARGIN

Mastering others is strength. Mastering yourself is true power.

—LAO TZU

As a kid, I had always assumed economics was just about money. Lots of money meant more control of the economics. Less money meant being under the control of people who have lots of money. Taking that further, economics was simply a science of power, control, and servitude—even if I didn't know what the word servitude meant. It was the stuff of Ann Rynd and Karl Marx but packaged in characters like Ebenezer Scrooge and Daddy Warbucks. I might not have gotten the memo on Adam Smith.

I realize now I had an incomplete understanding—go figure, a kid with an incomplete understanding. Economics *can* be about money, and money is often the engine of how anything gets produced, consumed, or distributed. The phrase "how is the economy doing?" is often framed on these nuts and bolts. But economics is not just about money or goods. It's about something more: economics is tethered to the motivations that lead to the production, consumption, and distribution of goods and services. The goods are the end result of our thinking at any given moment.

An example may help. Let's say it's 9 p.m. on a Tuesday. You'd really like Ben & Jerry's ice cream, but you don't have any at home. You're motivated and tech savvy, so you hop on your favorite delivery app and have somebody bring some to you. Joy! You start happily eating the ice cream, but it doesn't last long. You start to feel sadness and regret about doing something so impulsive late at night. You start to imagine your future tired and bloated self. Then you start to get upset with your thinking about your future self. A mental death spiral has started.

Meanwhile, Ben and Jerry are happy, and because you tip well, the delivery app and driver are also happy. You tell yourself you'll never eat Ben & Jerry's ice cream late at night again, until you forget three weeks later when you decide you were too hard on yourself and do it again. This time, you wise up and buy the pint at the grocery store and cut the delivery service out. You also eat it at 7 p.m. to save on the regret.

What just happened here? If we wanted to, we could examine the motivations of Ben, Jerry, and the driver. We could also look at the countless other companies that supplied the sugar, cream, transportation, and ink for cool pint art on the Ben & Jerry's container. The good/service exchange is simply *the result of* the motivational underpinnings. Ben, Jerry, and the driver are motivated to give you ice cream. The economics didn't start at the transaction. They started the moment your mind screamed "ice cream!" You could argue it started the moment Ben & Jerry screamed "ice cream," which led millions of others to do the same. Let that sink in for a second: the economics started with a thought. Understanding the underlying reason(s) for the thought and the money that comes with it will follow. This is a just right that will hopefully reveal itself soon.

As we all know, understanding human motivation is a tricky thing. But by understanding the reason(s), you begin to knock on the door of truth. Economics is often called the dismal science, but there's nothing dismal about searching for truth. There's a catch to the search though: not everyone wants us to know it.

What do I mean by "not everyone wants you to know it"? Growing up, I thought truth and transparency were fundamental to any economic transaction. If I'm buying a taco, I need to know the price and whether the person selling it to me is reliable, so it tastes good, and I don't get sick. That type of truth and transparency is vital. But there is an opposing tension to keep processes mysterious, to muddy the waters, and to make true knowledge as opaque as possible.

This might be strange, but there is power in keeping the masses in the dark. It's an important point and something I'll refer to later: "where there is mystery, there is margin." It's the profit—or margin—made from creating confusion and complexity in a system. Once it's clear, the goal for someone—or something—is to make a situation more complex, then the just right is to push against that complexity and settle the muddy waters, so they are clearer.

This may seem like a weird concept. It definitely was to me the first time I came upon it. Don't worry. I have some examples to help make it resonate. Hopefully, it helps in understanding the truth better.

I know that was a long preamble, but I hope it sets the stage for what comes next. This chapter will be about money, mystery, margin, and motivation, but not in the ways you'd expect. The search for a just right is by seeking clarity about the impact of all three.
It can often be sought by asking two basic questions:

1. What's the motivation of (fill in the blank)?

2. Who's benefiting or losing from the mystery?

Let's look at Reeta's case to illustrate these powers and questions in practice.

When I met Reeta after she ended up in the emergency room, her back was in pain after working with a chainsaw on her roof. They assigned her to me because a lifetime of smoking had sent her to the doctor one too many times.[13] The chainsaw fiasco was the last straw.

We talk over teleconference. She's in her midsixties, outgoing, funny, offbeat, and intelligent. She has a baritone voice made for radio and lounge singers. This is the way I imagine lifetime smokers *want* to sound. We talk for a bit about her experiences as a personal care attendant (PCA) working with the most vulnerable people over the years. I can tell it's made her wise and compassionate about caregiving. Sometimes caring for caregivers can feel very simpatico in that regard.

"I was an idiot for being up on that roof," she tells me early in our conversation.

---

13 I know I have an inordinate amount of smoker examples in the book. I can't help it. It's just that so many of the people who get assigned to me have the habit.

She knows I've read her record. I tell her she was bold for sawing tree branches on her roof and that sometimes the lines between being bold and feeling like an idiot can be blurry. This harkens back to the subjects of action and fate from the last chapter. To her, she chose to be up there, and nothing felt random about getting hurt. We weren't here to litigate her decisions.

We started talking about her injury and pain medications. At this point, she makes a conversational pivot.

"I know I'm a naughty girl," she offers.

It's not clear to me if this is about the chainsaw or the chain-smoking. I decide she means the chainsaw.

"I think you'd be up there again if you could," I reply.

She smiles.

"You're probably right," she laughs, the raspy hum of wet mucus filled lungs. Her intentions are clear.

We wrap up talking about her acute pain. She says she's better and off the muscle relaxants. I learn about her years at pain clinics, pain injections, and her weaning off narcotics. Her chronic pain is a different animal, but I'm shocked she has no further concerns. She seems to have clarity there. We move on to her other concerns: her breathing and cigarette smoking.

"It was easier getting off the opiates than getting off these damn cigarettes!" she complains.

She's earnest in all the attempts. She tells me stories about all the remedies—gums, lozenges, patches, and pills. She's not interested in "the holistic stuff."

My training kicks in, and I ask her the standard quit questions. Do you have a quit date? Have you thought about quitting with somebody else? Can you find someone in your life to help as an accountability partner?

She's heard them all. She says she'll "work on it," and that's that. In the end, I get the last say, telling her to pick a quit date and circle it on the calendar where she can see it. I'm not confident she'll follow through.

We move on and discuss the breathing medicines she wants but can't afford. Many of her trips to the doctor are for emergencies she may otherwise be able to avoid. If only she could pay for them.

I review her insurance plan and discuss the intricacies of deductibles and co-pays. Sometimes I feel glassy-eyed myself at all the terms. Do people really want to know? Probably not. In Reeta's case, she just wants me to solve the problem of helping her breathe easier. Sometimes, my job feels like a financial counselor mixed with a lung support specialist.

I review the fine print anyway, and she nods in understanding. We make plans to fix the cost issue in two different ways. For one inhaler, she uses a coupon she can take to the pharmacy for a discount, bypassing her insurance entirely. For the other inhaler, I switch treatments to something more affordable that her insurer will give her a better deal on. We also make plans to sign her up for a medication assistance program.

She's appreciative and I am ready to wrap up, but she's got one more thing on her mind. Our conversation veers into the perplexing state of the health system and the cost of some medications. I find this happens with some of the people I meet. They hold me captive as an audience of one to rail on a system that is off the rails. When she's done, she finishes with a poignant comment.

"I wonder how many people don't receive the type of help they need and are left to suffer because they don't know this stuff."

It's an interesting thought and a wise one. She probably realizes there are a legion of Reeta's out there; chainsawing, chain-smoking women who can't kick the habit, at least not just yet. There are people out there who just want the best chance to breathe but can't unlock the mystery of a broken system—sorry again, Walter Cronkite.

I meet Reetas often and sense peril closing in on them. The sticker shock of their medicines plays one part in that feeling. In the worst circumstances, people come out of a hospital or emergency room with broken bodies, picking up the smoldering remains of their health. Their recovery, if it goes well, comes with rest, physical therapy, good food, financial security, comradery, and medicines. When it goes poorly, patients sometimes scrape together money from donations, shrinking savings accounts, or family loans. Or it doesn't come at all. In the US, health care is the leading cause of bankruptcy (Cussen 2021). Without money, treatments stop on their own. Lack of money is motivation to stop treatment. The mystery is in wondering how we got here.

With all this weighing on their mind, the search for just right can seem like a futile journey. Health and money lead to questions that cut to the heart of money and motivation. Do I purchase this medicine or skimp on the food bill? Do I skip that lab test because I can't afford it? Health care is the high stakes collision of the money, motivation, and mystery aspects of economics. Because the stakes with health are so high, it offers a good incubator to search for clarity. It might help to explore Reeta's tale more closely.

For Reeta, motivation for the groups making the inhalers seem clear. Between 2013 and 2018, the average cash price for inhalers rose from around $280 to $380 (Marsh 2020). As of March 2022, the average cash price for Reeta's Advair inhaler in the United States was $648. That same Advair inhaler in Canada was $140 during the same time period (Mikulic 2022). Although it's true that many individuals in the United States have insurance, many states have between 10 to 20 percent of asthma patients who have either partial or no insurance coverage. And the self-reported data of people reporting cost issues with their treatments are as high as 28 to 48 percent (Centers for Disease Control and Prevention 2013). There is no mystery. Somebody has done the math, and there is a profit to be made from higher-cost treatments, even if one-in-five to one-in-ten aren't using them for financial reasons. There is margin—profit—in keeping the status quo, even if that means people like Reeta don't always access their medicine.

Looking at the inhaler market historically reveals more motivation and more mystery. What becomes clear is that the endless back and forth is intended to create that mystery. In the early 2000s, manufacturers reformulated inhalers to meet environmental standards. This sounds altruistic and, in some respects, it was. But it came with an opportunity to repackage the same medicines at a higher cost with no actual benefit to the people using them (Rosenthal 2013). To understand the inhaler market is to be lost in contracting quirks, patent extensions, and buzz phrases from manufacturers on prices such as "closely linking price." It's all mud in the water. It's also code for "we charge that price because we can." It's the creation of mystery—don't worry, I'll get to the mystery later—because the motivation is to make money.

I wish we could say this problem is isolated to breathing medications, but unfortunately, it's not. More mystery can be found in the pricing of another lifesaving medicine: insulin.

The cost of insulin is high. There's no mystery in that. Looking at motivation and money will reveal similar underpinnings. This serves as a launching point to look at the mystery further.

"My insulin is over $400 per month. I can't afford that, and I'm going to run out in two days. What am I going to do?"

I had met Sylvia at the medical clinic, and there was no mystery about what the focus of our visit was going to be about. Sylvia was in her late seventies. She had a thick Afro-Caribbean accent, and her hair was done up just so. Sylvia had worked in a cafeteria before retiring five years ago. She spent her days watching TV and spending time with her many grandkids.

Her diabetes control wasn't great, but optimal was a secondary concern at the moment. A complete stop in her insulin would almost surely mean a trip to the emergency room or worse. While there was no mystery in what to do, there was some mystery in how to do it.

"Let's look at your insurance first before we start making plans to change anything," I said.

I was hoping to project enough calm to help her feel the same. It was hard to tell through our surgical masks whether it was working.

I swiveled my computer screen so we could both see it together. I pulled up the online resources aimed at showing Sylvia what her options were, like a smart shopper who knows where to get the best deals. This is often a mystery unless you know exactly where to look.

"I see what's going on here," I said.

I showed her the insurance plan she had, the high deductible, and the high amount she had to pay for insulin. We discussed the insurance change she'd recently made. I calculated out where the $400 came from and what to expect for the rest of the year. I was trying to make the mystery of how we got here less muddy. Sometimes the how we got here, in service of clarity, just motivates individuals to become more anxious.

"Isn't there anything else we can use?" she said.

She was reluctant to switch, but she was desperate for something.

We reviewed her options. I explained it would require some hard truths: first, we'd have to switch the type of insulin she received, the insulin doses she took, the time of day she gave herself shots, and when she checked her blood sugar levels. I explained all this was inconvenient but would keep her out of the hospital at a price she could afford. She was reluctant but agreed after seeing the $350 she'd save. Money can have that type of motivating effect.

After laying the groundwork for the next two days, we started into what the next two months and next two years would look like. We reviewed programs aimed at getting her current insulin for free, given her income levels. We also reviewed smart shopper tools so she could buy better health insurance next year.

Slowly, the mysteries began to clear for Sylvia. I could start to feel her anxiety come down, surgical masks and all.

She thanked me with that Afro-Caribbean accent. We made plans to meet to see how the change would go. We kept her diabetes afloat as we explored long-term solutions. I was clear that care was not the primary challenge. This was a potential crisis where the mystery of price was driving everything.

Before searching for just right, it would be helpful to appreciate how things got just wrong. Some of those things include why we have Sylvias coming to the doctor unable to afford insulin in the richest country in the world, and how reasonable people making presumably reasonable decisions created mystery and money with complexity. Like describing mud, it can be challenging. Most would offer it's a mix of sand, silt, and dirt. But all you can think of the moment you see it is that it's slimy and messy. Describing the mud beyond the feelings it invokes is an exercise in finding clarity.

Much has been written about what goes into the price of insulin. Here are the facts: the average price of a vial of Humalog brand insulin has gone up from $21 in 1996 to $275 in 2019 (Stanley 2019). The three largest companies who make insulin, Sanofi, Eli-Lilly, Novo Nordisk, maintain a 95 percent share of the market (IQVIA Inc. 2021). There are no rules governing the prices they can set. They have taken an invention "sold"—only because the discovers at the University of Toronto couldn't donate it—for one dollar in 1921 and developed "similar" products at exorbitant prices (Diabetes UK 2022). Manufacturers are one source for the price Sylvia pays, but they are not the only ones.

The insurer also helps determine the price. To do that, the insurer hires a middleman called a pharmacy benefit manager (PBM) to negotiate that price. The PBM talks with the manufacturer on the price with the hopes of bringing the price down, which is often done in the form of an applied rebate (Thomas 2016). Theoretically, the rebate lowers the price of the medicine for the patient. Lower prices get passed on to the insurer, which then gets passed along to the employer and patient. The PBM takes a small cut for their negotiating prowess. The problem is solved and everybody's happy, at least in theory.

Does this sound complicated? Believe it or not, the description above is the scaled-down version. Don't forget the government (Medicare and Medicaid) and not just insurers are involved in both setting prices and negotiating discounts for themselves. The government is also a purchaser—think of veterans' affairs hospitals—and a regulator for hospital drug prices in some instances. Then there are what are called "specialty drugs"—for, example, infusions given to cancer patients or people with rare conditions—which have their own pricing and incentive structure.

The result of all this innovation is a level of complexity that no one person can understand. And that complexity is the point, at least to those who hope to make money off the mystery. The mystery is so beyond comprehension that money and profit margin are there for anyone willing to carve out a niche and make margin the goal. The incentive in the system is not for clarity, or care, it's for mystery because the primary motivation lies with money. Remember the quote from Walter Cronkite from the introduction?

America's health care system is neither healthy, caring, nor a system.

The status quo serves the winners, not the people.

The following picture helps illustrate the incentive structure. There are no U-shaped curves here as Pic. 15 on page 121 illustrates. But I'll get to searching for just right soon. Hopefully, the first part in seeing complexity serves mystery and margin clearly.

Sylvia's Path to Get Insulin

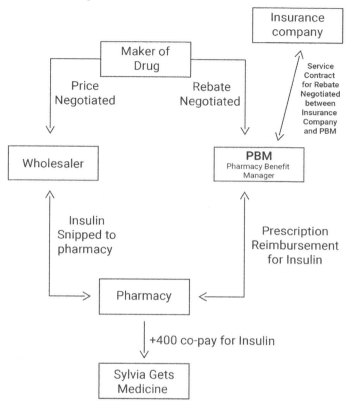

Pic. 15.

To be fair, the rules of the healthcare system—sorry again, Walter Cronkite—are common elsewhere. Rebate structures exist in other industries, a good example being what exists between car manufacturers and car dealers. Multiple prices are set for the same product in many other industries. Anybody who's seen different prices on the same box of pasta at two different grocery chains in the same town can appreciate it. Middlemen, like PBMs, also exist as negotiating entities across many industries. If you've ever hired a real estate agent to sell your home, you've encountered this firsthand. Medicines like inhalers and insulin are not exceptions as high-cost medicines. Insulin and inhalers do not even come close to cracking the list of the top twenty most expensive medications. Knowing all this, there is still clarity about the motivation. The reason the price of insulin has almost doubled from 2012 to 2019 is that manufacturers are allowed to do it (Entis 2019). They increase it because both manufacturers and PBMs stand to make more money by increasing the price. There are margins to be made and complexity—or mystery—in the general public about how they do it. What's the result? Individuals like Sylvia are left in the margins, worried about an abundant and once inexpensive treatment whose innovation was given away one hundred years ago for humanity's benefit. Where's the humanity in that?

As I've thought about the Sylvia and Reeta situations further, it grounded me in how fortunate my family has been to afford the care we've received in our life. It also helped me understand my own motivation and relationship to money. Examining your own motivations and mystery is important in any just right search of your own. Here's a portal into mine.

Let's be clear from the beginning: I've never had to suffer financial angst around my health like Reeta or Sylvia. I've been continuously working either part-time or full-time since I was fifteen. I've never stopped working or been laid off. I've never had doors slammed when I signed up for entry-level work. The jobs have varied—swimming pool construction, washing dishes, loading freight into airplanes, cold-calling high school kids for campus visits, driving a forklift, working as a pharmacy technician, and now a pharmacist—but the theme of finding and keeping work has been the same. Along the way, I've enjoyed the security of knowing that after I work, a set amount of money will end up in my bank account. That security was a foundational motivator to keep going. I was motivated to make money, the only mystery being whether I'd want a job as a career.

My first job paid four dollars and twenty-five cents per hour. I felt filthy rich when I got my first paycheck, the motivation being to save up for my first car. Little did I know, I'd be sinking dollar after dollar into a 1985 Ford Tempo for things like insurance, repairs, and gas money. The workings of insurance and car repair were a mystery, but there was comfort in knowing financial ruin was not close. I could take my lumps before the stakes and obligations of growing up got bigger.

Looking back, the truth about money, mystery, motivation, and margin could be boiled down to one word: freedom. Feeling little restraint while meeting the expectations of others—whether that's an employer, the tax man, family, or charity—has been a constant source of liberation when it's met. When I can pay or donate something with little guilt, shame, or angst, it feels true, like some basic level of human trust has been met. It doesn't happen often, but searching for just right doesn't mean it happens. It just means recognizing it when it does.

A note about this subject: the volume of books written on personal finance feels almost endless. It is not an exaggeration that one can spend a lifetime thinking about how to make and save money. But making and saving money and truth are different things. While there are many truths, I'm going to focus on two that matter to many: happiness and fulfillment.

In the personal finance book, *Your Money or Your Life*, Vicki Robin and Joe Dominguez outline a relationship between spending and happiness that is nonlinear, meaning every dollar you spend brings you a little less happiness as you go. Just right is not a straight line and the truth—at least when it comes to happiness—is that more and more spending doesn't keep translating.

They also suggest that more spending does lead to more fulfillment—up to a point. But spending too much can actually have a negative impact on your quality of life. The authors suggest a "just right" to personal fulfillment—that is, being balanced in your life—that looks like Pic. 16 below:

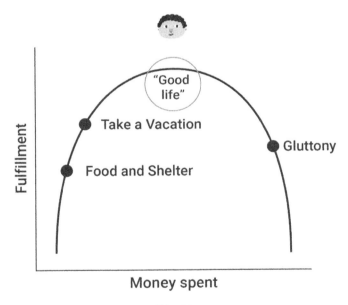

Fulfillment Curve

Pic. 16.

"It seems natural to assume that rich people will be happier than others," writes psychologists Ed Diener and Robert Biswas-Diener in the book *Happiness: Unlocking the*

Mysteries of Psychological Wealth. "But money is only one part of psychological wealth, so the picture is complicated."

There is a strong correlation between wealth and happiness. The authors say: "Rich people and nations are happier than their poor counterparts; don't let anyone tell you differently," they state at one point. Also, note that money's impact on happiness isn't as large as you might think. If you have clothes to wear, food to eat, and a roof over your head, increased disposable income has just a small influence on your sense of well-being.

To put it another way, if someone is living below the poverty line—$22,050 annual income for a family of four in 2009—an extra $5,000 a year can make a huge difference in their happiness. On the other hand, if a family earns $70,000 a year, $5,000 may be a welcome bonus, but it won't radically change their life.

For Reeta and Sylvia, not having the freedom to buy their medicine to breathe and treat their diabetes feels enormous because the need is basic, and the stakes are high. There is no mystery in that.

Now, terms like "happiness," "fulfillment," and "well-being" may feel semantic. What is the real difference when trying to sort out any personal truth? The just right search for money is about the need to understand its motivation but not at the expense of it becoming our master—to like Ben & Jerry's without being beholden to it.

If we've learned anything to this point, the truth is hard to figure out. Complexity shows up in strange places, from middlemen with hopefully good intentions to multiple prices for the same product. Organizations know this, and yet there's another complexity factor we haven't discussed that looms large in a just right search: choice, a subject we touched on in Chapter 6.

All the things that lead to choices, even if it's "ice cream," seem to matter in ways we barely consciously understand. The science of choice can reveal uncomfortable feelings and give us a false feeling of clarity when we make decisions. It's a powerful source for money, mystery, and motivation, and its underpinnings are similar to framing of statistics we reviewed in Chapter 3. Its search for just right is similar as well.

In a *Hidden Brain* podcast interview on the role of choice in decision-making, psychologist Eric Johnson described a research study he conducted evaluating car insurance purchases between residents of New Jersey and Pennsylvania. This sounds super boring, right? On the surface, yes, but the results help us understand choice better. By making the less expensive insurance option easier to choose in New Jersey, the less expensive plan was three times more popular than it was in Pennsylvania. The economic impact to Pennsylvania, just by the way the choice information was presented on a car insurance form, was estimated at about $2 billion in 2003. Think about that: a $2 billion form. Even designing a form can lead to mystery or clarity, depending on the motivation of individuals involved. The money involved is potentially massive.

The science of choice has also been demonstrated when selecting healthcare coverage, with poor decision "architecture"—that is, the tools and information that help us as consumers to make better decisions when signing up—costing taxpayers an estimated $10 billion per year (Johnson et al. 2014).

Extending this beyond choosing insurance offers more sobering news about fundamental decision-making around money. One study found the basics of personal finance to be challenging for a good percentage of Americans (Mitchell 2017). When asked three basic questions about personal finance, over half of the people over fifty years old got two out of three correct. Only about one-third got all three questions correct.

The motivation, especially to those early in life, needs to be in helping individuals understand basic financial choices better. Understanding misconceptions, something at the heart of Chapter 3, is something that can help sort out the mystery.

This chapter has been awash in words like money, mystery, motivation, truth, and choice. It's fair to ask where all these words get us. I shared the stories of Reeta and Sylvia, who were caught in a system—sorry again, Walter Cronkite—that is complex and mysterious and serves the motivations of the stakeholders who understand it, not the people whose product is being used. Where the mystery exists, so does the margin—profit—to be made. Just right means moving in the direction of simplicity, a counterforce to all the additional layers and middlemen intent on margin.

We also looked at the truth, how money is the result of "ice cream!" moments and understanding the underpinnings of those thoughts. They are at the heart/truth of any goods and services being sold and distributed. Understanding the metaphorical Ben and Jerry will help bring clarity for anyone willing to search. Mine is freedom. We looked at the happiness and fulfillment U-shaped curve more closely for other searches. The truth is search is a choice.

Finally, we looked at the idea of choice, a science with large economic consequences and worrisome trends for large-scale understanding. It was an opportunity to put a spotlight on the mystery and the motivation of complex choices, intentionally cultivate systems to help people make more informed decisions, and educate our young on the basics of personal finance.

Economics is a great discipline because it gets at the heart of what it means to be human. How goods and services are distributed are a proxy for their human underpinnings. It's us at our most basic. It may feel disappointing to end a chapter with no clear solutions offered. I'm not here with the answers. I'm here with the mirror, holding it up for us to see ourselves. The search for just right (and ice cream) is all around us. The search for truth may be aided by where we're going next, to a subject filled with things understood and others lost in translation.

CHAPTER 8

COMMUNICATION—
THE POWER OF CROWDS
AND PERSONAL WISDOM

―――

*Speaking with kindness creates confidence, thinking with kind-
ness creates profoundness, giving with kindness creates love.*

—LAOZI

I want to start out with a thought exercise. I hope it's fairly
easy. No extreme brain teasers here. It's helpful to join along
because it has implications for everything that's coming. I'll
be referencing back to it later in the chapter.

I want everyone to think about the last time they were
left feeling not right after a human interaction.

It could have been from earlier today, the past few days,
or many years ago, but don't overthink it. It could be something that, in hindsight, seems trivial or otherwise looms
large in life. Maybe it was a text message that got taken out
of context or a system miscommunication at work where
people didn't meet expectations. Maybe somebody's tone of
voice struck you as rude at the grocery store, or maybe it was
a child not cleaning up after themselves and then erupting

when they were reminded of it. Do you have your thought? Great, hold on to it for a bit as we explore the broad themes of what happened.

When living through communication stinkers, a few things generally come up. The first is to wonder how something got lost in translation. If it's a big deal, I'll replay the "what exactly happened here?" sequence in a constant loop, trying to leave out the emotions to help me clarify what to do next. Often, my imaginary self says the just right thing at just the right moment, like a movie action hero or quick-witted comedian. Either way, I'm in my head a lot with very mixed results. Did I mention I watched too many movies as a kid?

The following will be an exploration of what gets lost when miscommunicating to understand the roots of the loops we play in our heads. The search will take us into how we communicate at work, through translators, in games, and with ourselves. It will feel a little strange until it all, hopefully, comes together.

Because this book is framed in relationships and health, I'm going to start there again. My hope is the themes have applicability in what gets lost in our everyday lives. Let's meet Sheila, someone whose intentions to communicate were good, but things got lost along the way.

"I feel like crap," Sheila told me. "And I don't know what's going on. I'm hoping you can help."

Before explaining why Sheila felt this way, it's best to explain how she got here. It started when she developed pain in her abdomen, leading her to go to the emergency department to find out why. What they eventually found led her to the operating room, where they removed her gallbladder.

She then lost a significant amount of blood due to a surgical complication and an infection requiring antibiotics. This left Sheila confused about how both came to be.

Her confusion continued after she got out of the hospital. First, she received conflicting directions on when to stop the antibiotics after surgery, a by-product of being seen by two different surgeons during her hospital stay. There was also the important blood thinner she'd been on prior to the surgery. She wasn't sure if it was safe to start taking it again. Because both of these decisions involved medicines, Sheila was hoping I could help her find what had been lost in translation. She was also hoping to have me sort out when she could expect to start feeling better because nobody had given her a timeline.

"I can see you've been through a lot," I said. "We'll get answers to these questions in time."

We first decided to clarify the plan for her blood thinner. During the interview, I asked if there was blood in her stool. She said yes. When I asked if this had come up with other caregivers, she said no. The only reason it had come up now was that I had just asked. She hadn't previously brought it up because she was told she would see blood for a while, but she wasn't sure how long "a while" was. Translating meant something new now that she was home and monitoring things on her own.

We next talked about her antibiotic. She was still running a low-grade fever. We discussed the other signs of infection. It was clear she needed to stay on the treatment, and I told her so. I agreed to review the duration of antibiotics with her doctor, who she was due to see soon.

Sheila was frustrated. This was not new to me because this was not my first encounter with her. When I saw her eighteen months prior, she'd experienced similar challenges about miscommunication with her care. In that instance, it was about her heart rhythm and the medications she tried that had failed. She felt a sense of not being heard, its own form of care lost in translation. I wasn't sure if it was a miscommunication or lack of progress, but we decided to focus on the things she could control. She improved her diet. We talked about seeing the doctor again about a surgical option. We adjusted the heart rhythm medicine under the direction of her heart specialist. For a period, she was feeling much better and feeling heard in her challenges.

Now the situation was different, but the feeling was all the same. Sheila felt like she was in a bad sequel when the original film was never all that good either. We discussed how that felt, and we again discussed how the best way forward was to get to the business at hand.

In the end, we made plans to restart her blood thinner and stop the antibiotic. In time, Sheila did get better. It's hard to know whether better communication impacted her conditions. Things were definitely safer and more intentional. It made me wonder if what gets lost are not plans but sentiments and trust.

We finished talking about how to get her trust back and how to advocate for herself in the future. She was diplomatic and shared that it was nobody's fault. She felt the people involved were working hard in her best interest. We parted ways, and she said she'd message me in the future if anything came up, just as she'd done before.

I left her with a good-natured, "I hope never to see you again."

Even while helping with the hard decisions of her care, I left my second encounter with Sheila much like the first: did anything we discuss make a difference in what gets lost? How does a fractured system break the patterns playing out over and over? It's a just right search veering in many directions. I promised some of them would be strange. Let's take a look a little further at what directions Sheila took me in.

What felt imbalanced and not right in Sheila's case? There were many people in the crowd but no fingers to point. I did the quiz math: there were eight doctors who saw her in the weeks during and after her hospitalization. There were dozens of nurses, therapists, assistants, and, yes, a pharmacist who'd interacted with her over a two-week period. Competency did not appear to be the problem; while her surgery didn't go exactly as planned, everything seemed well-done and well-reasoned. Plenty of brain horsepower was in place, and there was nowhere to cast blame. Yet talking to Sheila felt like a collective loss. Maybe my expectations were too high. Maybe Sheila's expectations were too high.

Looking at it, what happened to Sheila reminded me of a thought experiment—this is where it gets strange.

It goes something like this:

Imagine you want to build the ultimate car. Cost is no barrier. To build it, you decide to take the best parts from all the various manufacturers. You hop on your private jet (because you can) to get started. First, you stop at the Volvo plant to get their chassis. Next, it's off to Honda to take their best suspension. Next, you fly to Italy to get the Ferrari engine, then stop by the Tesla plant to steal the electric motor secrets to add to the Ferrari engine (Elon Musk signs off). Finally, you stop at the Ford plant for their lightweight and sturdy car frames. You finally fly home to start assembling the super car with all these best parts. You're giddy with excitement; people are going to flip when they see this car! You begin to assemble it and realize you have a big problem: none of the car parts fit together! They require modifications, and none of them seem to work. You're mad and rich, and being rich means things are supposed to work out. Not in this case. In the end, you're left with an expensive and perfectly engineered piece of junk. You scrap the project. But hey, you've still got that private jet.

Heard this one before? It comes up all over the place. At work, it's in amassing all the smartest people who don't work well in teams. In sports, it's getting the best players whose talents don't mesh well on the field.[14] It can also play out in music where the virtuoso drummer and guitar players from other bands get together to make a terrible album. It's setting up two people you like on a blind date who seem compatible on paper but end up on the date from hell.

In the search for the better car and the better Sheila, two things seem obvious, so obvious that some will roll their eyes that I wrote it. That's okay. I'll take my chances. It's my book, after all.

The first is looking at anything we intentionally do. Communication often boils down to the space between thoughts and words or thoughts and actions. Let that sink in for a moment because it's the space where the just right happens, where we see better what's lost.

For the car, it's the space that looks at how parts fit together, just as it would for the sports teams. Next comes the search itself, which is finding the best available solutions

---

14 At least this provides something for podcasts and talk radio to speculate on.

based on that understanding. It's taking fit and breaking it into smaller parts, a curiosity theme we explored in Chapter 2. For the car or sports teams, this means calling in the statisticians and engineers and making sure they fit together as well.

What about intentions and solutions for Sheila? Come to find out researchers have studied the understanding of the components in health care that apply to Sheila, much like the car parts or sports team that didn't come together. It's called fragmentation and is worth understanding in any just right search. It gets at the space between thought and action.

Healthcare fragmentation is a phrase used to describe the collection of misalignments and miscommunications that happen in health (Schmidt 2019). It takes on different meanings depending on perspective. It's the many loose strands of miscommunication leading to big frays. It could be a doctor who can't see a test result. It could be the nurse who can't get a hold of a patient about a critical test. It may be seeing three different medical specialists and still not understanding the next steps in care.

Fragmentation may sound trivial, but it's not. One study estimated the cost of fragmentation for Medicare patients showed an average cost difference of $10,396 for the most fragmented care versus $5,854 for the least (Frandsen et al. 2015). Roughly $5,000 times sixty-two million people on Medicare in 2020 equals a lot of money (Yang 2022). The space is needed to address fragmentation.

If we know fragmentation moves us toward more loss in translations, how do we begin to move closer? What follows is incomplete and fragmented—pun intended. A sharp right turn away from health care is required because when it comes to understanding just right, it's helpful to look to other industries to provide guideposts. It may just help with setting right what went wrong with Sheila or at least give her the space she deserves.

One other industry is the online gaming world, where the "best" group sizes have been analyzed—a U-shaped curve is coming! Come to find out, many games start to follow a U-shaped distribution for frequency of player interactions like in Pic. 17 below. This is shown in the following picture.

Gaming Just Right Group Size

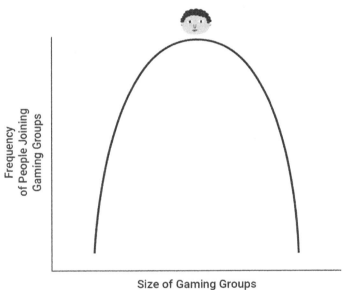

Pic. 17.

What this shows is that for many public online games, gaming groups initially swell as players join. But after a certain number of players, interest in joining declines. The number of players depends on the game; for role-playing games, the number is smaller (four to six), and for larger first-person shooter games, the forums may be larger (closer to fifty or one hundred).[15]

The exact number isn't the point. The point is that real intent matters when trying to create the best player experience. More "just rights" are possible when the right goal and space to understand the user is clear. It's not just all about the best graphics or gameplay.

Video games are not the only place looking at communication and group size. Anthropologists and business development specialists have also tried to understand how humans have evolved to communicate. The most popular of these searches is the Dunbar number (Webber 2020). The Dunbar number represents a limit—or just right—to the number of people with whom one can maintain stable social relationships. For close friends, the just right number is around five, and for names you can put faces to—most famously—it's around 150. Being a business leader means understanding how groups work together and how many. Leaving space for ideal team sizes may help assign the right number of people to the project.

Where does this leave us? Or Sheila? If fragmentation is the intention to look at a problem, how do video games and anthropology help in the search for what's lost? Where are the engineers and statisticians to take action?

For Sheila, it means assigning her a small team to manage her challenges instead of relying on just one provider of a large, loosely connected group. One engineering health

---

15   This is a gross oversimplification. If you still don't understand what any of this means, ask someone under the age of twenty-five to explain it to you.

project is called complex case management, which is where a small group of clinicians are tasked with improving care and reducing fragmentation. Although the story is not fully written, studies have shown a 37 percent reduction in cost when the sickest people are assigned a complex case management team (Powers et al. 2020). In a sense, the principles involved in video games and Dunbar numbers have made it to health. The sickest people need small teams who know their story inside and out. It may also help that imaginary car come together just right.

If this feels too academic, too big picture, too not applicable to day-to-day life, never fear. Much more can be learned on the search through thinking about things like wisdom and mastery, which is where we're going next. It may even have something to reveal in the most unexpected of places: through a translator.

Communicating through a translator is an ecosystem all its own. It requires an extra layer of communication just to make sure the listener understands the words. That doesn't begin to explain all the other opportunities for information to get lost.

Amina was a good example. When she came into the exam room with the translator, only her eyes were visible through the hijab and mask. Her robe colors were dark and understated. She had no facial expression to read. I prepared myself that coming to a common understanding may take a little extra time.

As we sit down, I can sense she's trying to figure out whether to trust me. I realize this as a way of cutting through translators to something beyond words. Her eyes are so bright and close that I can see the recent cataract procedure in her left eye, which aligns with the "blurriness" that I'd read in her medical record. It felt like a good metaphor for where our conversation could go.

I start out by asking the translator to ask her what brings her in.

"I have a fear of everything: fear of medicines, fear of side effects, fear of getting old, fear of not understanding what's going on in my body. I'm afraid I'll lose sight in my left eye. It all feels too much."

I hesitate about where to begin. I'm aware of every body movement she makes. In this woman with one functional eye who can't read or write in her native Somali, let alone English, she's using her other senses to communicate. I resolve myself to do the same.

I tell her my worry is about her diabetes.

"Can we begin there?" I ask.

She agrees. I sense she's happy I've confessed something too and given her a place to start.

I tell her the blood sugars in her body are very high. I explain how this affects her entire health: the pain she feels, the fears she has about getting old, the lab tests she wants to make sure are okay.

"I do not want to check my sugars. I am afraid of those needles on my fingers," she tells me through the translator.

I can tell she's had this conversation with caregivers before. She's ready to stop the discussion before it starts.

"Sure, I can appreciate that. What about monitoring your sugar with a patch you wear on your arm?" I said.

Her eyes brighten a bit.

"Yes! I've heard of these. Some people in my building have them. I'm scared of putting it on. Does it hurt?"

I explain most patients don't experience pain. She's interested but still not convinced. I'm at a crossroads. I decide to turn to the British to help.

I tell her I want us to watch a five-minute video together. It's in English, but it shows a British woman doing the very thing I'm asking her to do. As she's watching the video, I'm mostly watching her because I've already seen the video countless times. We watch the British narration with no language translation, just a woman taking a product out of the box and placing the sensor on her body. During the video, I offer a few comments that the translator reviews with her. Afterward, she agrees to start it. I begin the process of ordering it.

We review the rest of her medicines. We make plans to see each other again soon to review the results. I ask her if she needs help with putting the patch on once she receives it. She says no; she will have her friends help her put the patch on. She leaves with a smile I can only see in her eyes, something I try to hold on to.

Conversations like the one I had with Amina are commonplace. Two people speaking two different languages trying to make sense of one another. I've had hundreds of translator conversations in my life. Countless other people have, too. Many are transactional: you ask for help with X, I give you help with Y. But looking closer, translator conversations reveal something more fundamental about how we search with more intention and space on what's lost.

One intention is called the Wisdom of Crowds. This may seem counterintuitive. What do crowds have to do with three people together in a visit? And why does it apply to Amina, the translator, and me? A jellybean guessing contest may help to better explain how personal interactions are rarely just about the conversation in that moment.

For those unfamiliar with a jellybean guessing contest, here's how it works. A group of people—the more the better—are asked to guess the number of jellybeans in a jar. People look in the jar—without opening it or sharing their guess—write their guess, and place it in a separate jar. The person who guesses the closest to the number of jellybeans wins the game. Simple, right? Most people have taken part in these either in a work breakroom or at school at some point. When participating in these contests, I hope for two outcomes: 1) I win the contest, or 2) I am best friends with the person who won, and they will share their winnings.

These contests can be fun, especially if held in a public area where people tend to congregate. But the jellybeans aren't the coolest part—maybe. What's amazing is how the aggregated guesses compare to any individual guess. What happens, assuming no outside biases or influences, is the aggregate or "crowd" comes much closer to the exact answer than any one individual when averaging the results. The bigger the crowd, the more accurate they become.

Graphically, it looks like this U-shaped curve in Pic. 18 on the next page moving toward a version of just right.

In James Surowiecki's book *The Wisdom of Crowds*, he argues that larger groups can be more intelligent than smaller ones. He makes a compelling case, using examples from broad subjects such as finance, finding lost submarines, and improving Google searches. The Wisdom of Crowds is meant to illustrate the power of collective thinking on a common problem.

Unbiased crowds can be collectively wiser in some situations, moving us closer toward right, which is great. So, what does that have to do with me, Amina, and the translator?

Wisdom of Crowds

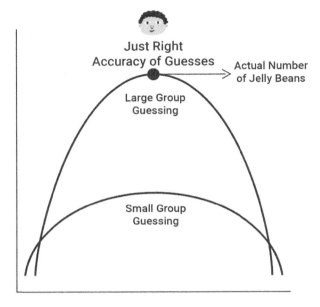

Pic. 18.

One focuses on crowds all around us. The other focuses on the crowd within.

The "crowd" around is the translator system that found me someone who understood Amina. The translator, in this case, worked with Amina and was familiar with her fears. Having her there was not an accident and takes a crowd to set up. Holding space for the needs of a visit and being intentional helps allow the best chance of a good action.

Next, was the computer screen where a white British actor sold an East African woman on the value of putting on a glucose monitor. While intently watching the video, I began to see how intentional the woman's hands were on the device to make it straightforward. It serves us well to appreciate how many "crowds" came together with the right tools at the just right moment to make a skeptical person more willing.

While the translator and videos show the crowd around us, the crowd within us comes from deliberate practice. Hundreds of interactions with translators over the years are the deliberate practice training ground for a specific form of expertise. Much has been written about learning and mastery, in statements about ten thousand hours of practice (Clear 2022). Graphically, mastery in education and achievement can take on a U-shaped curve all its own, which is shown in Pic. 19 below. The inner crowd of expertise can culminate in looking someone in the eye, asking permission, and knowing a video is better than my explanation. Its leaving space to trust the quality of the translator's rapport and the videos.

Achievement

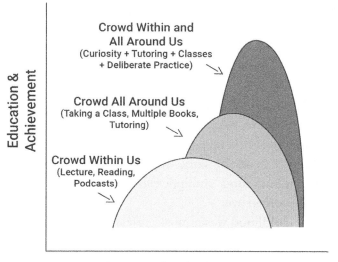

Crowd Within and
All Around Us
(Curiosity + Tutoring + Classes
+ Deliberate Practice)

Crowd All Around Us
(Taking a Class, Multiple Books,
Tutoring)

Crowd Within Us
(Lecture, Reading,
Podcasts)

Education &
Achievement

Distribution of Achievement Scores

Pic. 19.

Up to this point, the challenges with Amina and Sheila have been more professional and academic. This approach of looking at intention is helpful but uninspiring to some. I hope to remedy that.

Remember when I discussed not feeling right after a human interaction? Below, I reevaluate a big "not right" of my own. As you'll see, I've had some time to think about it. My search was aided by something I have no control over—time—and something I do—intention, space, and action. Maybe it will help better reveal your own search a little more.

I lost my best friend when I was fifteen years old. His death was not sudden, at least not in the way we think of young people dying either by accident or suicide. Doctors diagnosed him with cancer just as I was learning how to drive, his diagnosis coming near his fifteenth birthday. Our friendship started at six years old. Our ages were separated by three months. Our homes were only separated by fifteen feet. I can't remember many childhood moments that didn't involve him.

Growing up, we were obsessed with the same childhood things: 4 square, baseball cards, cartoons, and the GI Joe Aircraft Carrier. He was in many ways the perfect childhood friend: silly in all the same ways I was, kind, loyal, smart, a lover of junk food, and quick to forgive and forget if we didn't see eye to eye.

Our childhood was almost perfect: we'd play, disagree about something, then play some more. We'd get on our bikes and pedal everywhere, the neighborhood up the road, the railroad tracks, the comic bookstore, Blockbuster Video. He loved the Detroit Tigers. I loved the Chicago Cubs. We both loved Michael Jordan. There seemed to be no way this person wouldn't be in my life for the rest of our days.

As we got older, our obsessions moved to other things. Before he got sick, we talked endlessly about our first cars and the freedom they'd provide. We'd even started mowing lawns together to make money. I got my driver's permit the summer I turned fifteen. He got diagnosed with cancer three months later, just as he would have been getting his.

I remember going up to the hospital the year he was sick. My mom—bless her—took me after school or sports practice. I remember so little of what we talked about. I felt I had landed on Mars: the antiseptic smells, the blinking lights, the people who seemed hellbent on disfiguring my friend, not making him better.

Working in health care was a million miles away. I now understand this was a protective measure in my brain, a way of shielding hurt. I was, in a way, lost in my own translation as a kid. Any type of wisdom was many years in the making.

Looking back, I did not have the language to talk to him about how much I cared. I had a teenager's naivete that things would get better. I had a teenager's bitterness when it didn't. I still wonder if he knew how I felt. Through the antiseptic smells and his suffering, I could sense my innocence had been shattered.

I often think on how much I didn't say to him, to his family, to my family. Why do words not come out of our mouths when we want them to? This was somebody who might as well have been my brother; our lives were so intertwined. What made me so tongue-tied?

One of my last memories was sleeping next to his bed days before he died. They brought him home to pass away in his living room, a fact I was still in denial about. I had never told him how much I'd miss him. By then, he was an unrecognizable shell. When I spoke to him, I wasn't sure how much got through.

The last night will live with me forever. He shouted out in the dark how he wasn't ready to die. I heard him, watched his mother rush in to comfort him, and stroke his head and arm. I buried my head in my pillow. I imagined all those movies we'd watched together would give me the just right thing to say to help ease his pain, but nothing appeared. No form of media or higher power would give me what I felt I needed at that moment.

It's taken me many years to understand what got lost in my fifteen-year-old translation. Watching others move through grief, reading about it, and experiencing it again has been an important teacher. In a way, time and the Wisdom of Crowds have also helped me translate my feelings. What I've finally been able to find space for is this: without grief, we do not fully understand love, without time, we cannot find perspective, and without suffering, we cannot find truth. I'm clear in my love for a friend I lost, even if it took me years to get those simple words out right. That feels like something worth revealing.

Remember that exercise at the beginning of the chapter when I asked everyone to think about an interaction that didn't feel right? Whatever was chosen, hopefully, I've shown that searching for "just right" communication takes on many forms. It also takes understanding what's lost while being intentional and leaving space in what's found.

This search can take multiple iterations. It may mean finding crowds who put the just right tools in place in just the right way to unlock a better way. How this looks could vary. It could be the mentor at work who seems to have "been there, done that" with just about everything. It could be the divorced friend who's sanguine about the trauma of relationship loss. It could be books and academic research evaluating the communication conundrum, like the Dunbar number or the right number of players in a video game. Scientists are using crowds every day to help make better decisions; they just have bad PR and decide to call them studies. They'd be better off calling them searches.

Next, we are going to leave the world of intention, space, and action and head into the subject of self-improvement. This dovetails into the mastery within the subject we just touched on. It will be a further examination of how we get good at anything and the just right set of circumstances that are need. It will delve into the very nature of how we really know something, when we put up defenses in the pursuit of knowledge, and how we move into something more right.

CHAPTER 9

SELF-HELP—USING MIRRORS AND CHALLENGING CONVENTIONS

Do you have the patience to wait until your mud settles and the water is clear?

—LAO TZU

Logic would suggest that a career helping people with bad health would lead to clarity about what it takes to find good health. Health care, at its core, is about helping people. Taking the thought experiment further, it would mean healthcare workers would all be the fittest, smartest, and most well-adjusted humans on Earth. It would be a case study in the power of applying the lessons of others to better themselves—only if it was that simple.

If health care is a vehicle toward some version of self-help, it's not in the platitudes, bumper stickers, or sound bites about "killing it." Yes, health care is about fixing organs and bones and giving drugs and comfort to reduce suffering. Any caregiver will tell you stories about how satisfying these "fix it" moments can be. I know I have mine. But the self-help "just right" that comes from health care, if such a thing exists, may simply be in holding up a mirror to reflect back on what our bodies are capable of doing on their own.

Stan was a good example of that. In his early fifties, Stan was in deep denial about his diabetes. He was also busy running an animal shelter business. He was a fortunate person in some respects, finding a profession he couldn't stop sharing his excitement about. I was a willing listener to his animal stories because I love animals too. But his work passion had led to health neglect. He was now starting to suffer the consequences of that indifference.

Initially, I focused on getting Stan to take medications one time per day. This may sound simple, but to Stan, this was no small feat. He was hesitant but agreeable after explaining the aid they could provide. The denial reached a peak when we talked about food. It reached a head when we started talking about the subtle differences between bananas and raspberries.

"Fruit is fruit!" Stan said somewhat incredulously. "I don't believe a banana is any better or worse for me than a raspberry."

Stan resisted medicines, then acquiesced. Food was another form of resistance.

"Maybe, but a raspberry is higher in fiber than a banana, so you might notice a difference in your blood sugars if you eat more berries," I offered.

Stan didn't want to challenge me on fruit trivia. But he didn't seem to want to change either. As the conversation continued, denial started to turn to bargaining.

"Bananas are easy to carry in my car. Maybe I just eat them instead as a snack," he offered.

He was looking for me to say it was okay. He wanted to bargain. It wasn't my choice, but I wasn't budging.

"That's fine, but I think you'd be best to switch to raspberries for a week and see what happens. You have your new glucose monitor that allows you to check all the time. Why don't you see for yourself?"

"Okay, I'll try it," he said. "I like this new monitor. The least I can do is put it to use."

He left the meeting with a new snack plan. When we talked on the phone, two weeks later, he was excited to talk about his progress.

"You were right about the berries!" he said. "My sugars haven't skyrocketed at all in my truck these past two weeks. I can't believe it!"

Animal excitement was now fruit excitement.

I didn't have the heart to tell him that regularly taking his medicines may have been helping or the regular monitoring he was now doing. I just expressed excitement. The slight shift closer to just right was coming in those moments alone in his truck—or opening his breakfast pill box.

Sometimes, the only way to help in health care is to hold the mirror up in just the right way. Let people adjust their view to see a better profile of themselves, making sure to stay out of view as they're doing it.

What's going on with Stan? What made him open to seeing himself differently? As a healthcare worker who's held up a lot of mirrors, I struggle to understand it sometimes. Sometimes I'd like to credit a Jedi mind trick. Truth be told, Stan is more of the exception than the rule; for every five Stans I meet, only one turns out like him. What's happening is one aspect of what many describe as self-help. If there's a mild allergy to the term, don't worry, there are others who agree. I'm one of them.

But Stan being receptive to helping himself is worth a closer examination. It reveals many things in the just right search. On one level, competence started to happen to Stan. The first level of competence came from his new electronic glucose monitor. Medical science is clear about continuous glucose monitors being helpful for many people with diabetes. The question is why. Most speculate the additional bodily information helps them make better health decisions about food and activity. I often liken them to windshield wiper fluid or Google Maps in your car. They are aids to better understand where we're going. Competence comes in a machine acting as a mirror.

On another level, surrender and acceptance of information about medicines and food helped Stan. The raspberry versus banana debate was a moment where Stan chose competence over his own confidence. He was open-minded enough to accept new information and not allow doubt to overwhelm him. He developed enough trust and rapport to believe it could work. This wasn't a trick mirror. It was a way of seeing more clearly. I often scratch my head in these situations. Is this what self-help means? Just right being just less stubborn and pigheaded when the situation calls for it?

The following U-shaped curve (Pic. 20 on the next page) may help explain Stan's experience with competence and confidence. Called the Dunning-Kruger Effect, it was first described in 1999 by Cornell University psychologists Dr. David Dunning and Dr. Justin Kruger (Psychology Today 2022). Its evaluation of bias holds clarity for the blind spots we all carry—or stubbornness that causes the muddy waters to stir up.

According to the theory, when somebody comes upon new information, their confidence level in that area significantly goes up. We're all subject to this bias. Remember in the introduction when I shared the idea of a just right between

Dunning Krueger Effect

Pic. 20.

novelty and familiarity regarding baby eye movement? This is the shiny new object that captures our attention. Maybe it was both familiar and complex enough to help us focus. We start by learning everything we can about it. But how much of this subject do we really understand at first?

Imagine listening to a podcast, watching a YouTube video, reading a *Reader's Digest* magazine, or reviewing a Wikipedia page. We can sometimes finish those novel experiences with a feeling of "Voilà! I get it!" This is Stan first putting on the glucose monitor. This is Goldilocks when she first enters the bears' home. This is fixing a clogged pipe and announcing we're master plumbers. It's patching a hole in a pair of pants and feeling like we're seamstresses. The buzz of new information and competence makes anyone blind to unknowns. Confidence soars, but competence is still a long way off.

For Stan, he walked into our first meeting in denial, brimming with confidence and feeling like he had all the right answers. Stan was Goldilocks just as she enters the bears' home. He despaired at needing to make changes in an already busy life. His move closer toward just right meant temporary despair in finding the more sustainable path.

Searching for just right, in one respect, is seeing where one lies on the U-shaped confidence/competence curve. For Stan, I imagine the Dunning-Kruger moments came slowly in the truck, thinking about food as he fussed over his dogs, inching ever closer away from despair toward expertise. Just right means taking momentary despair and translating it into action. What happens in that space of change, a subject we touched on in Chapter 8, is the inflection point of just right.

Please note: Drs. Dunning and Kruger did not design the Dunning-Kruger Effect for use as a self-improvement tool. But looking at its visual trajectory over time can be helpful in understanding where we lie in any type of change and where space is needed. Next, we're going to look at other U-shaped curves to better understand ourselves, including my discomfort with a topic I decided to write an entire chapter about. But first, a dive into the self-improvement industry.

Self-help is, by any measure, a big business. Market data estimates that the US self-improvement market was worth $11.6 billion in 2019, and forecasts expect a 6 percent average annual growth to $14 billion by 2025 (LaRosa 2021). An ecosystem of lecturers, coaches, weight loss programs, and retreat centers exists to help anyone in almost any area of personal improvement. In a sense, the self-help movement is an economic, intellectual, and emotional culture dedicated to the search for Goldilocks—or maybe not. Maybe it's a culture obsessed with winning and some notion of success. Remember earlier in Chapter 1 when I referenced a baby's eyes naturally gravitating toward a just right familiarity and complexity? In it, I made the argument that there's something hardwired in us attempting to find "just right." Well, it seems other U-shaped curves unconsciously apply in the pursuit of self-improvement.

The most popular example may be the Yerkes-Dodson Curve. Developed in 1908 by psychologists Robert M. Yerkes and John Dillingham Dodson, the law demonstrates an upside-down U-shape in performance and arousal like in Pic. 21 below. When arousal or stress goes up, so does

Performance

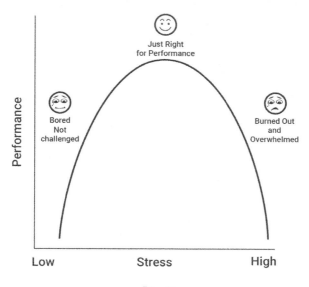

Pic. 21.

performance. When levels of arousal or stress become too high, performance decreases (Gino 2016). It seems when learning complex tasks, our adult brains aren't all that different from our infant brains in searching for just right. Research into this phenomenon has gone even further, down to the cellular level. Steroid production seems to match Yerkes-Dodson upside-down U-shaped curve for complex task learning (Wirth 2015). As our bodies pump out more steroid, complex performance goes up. But too much steroid seems to have the opposite effect. What's more, this just right steroid phenomenon has been linked to outcomes such as long-term memory formation and concentration. In some ways, our bodies are wired in the search for an improvement just right. Now if we could only be more intentional in the search for it.

Want more Goldilocks in the area of personal performance? Take the most self-help of enterprises, exercise, a $32 billion industry in 2020 (Gough 2021). Researchers have found that the best "dose" to prevent heart disease may be about 150 minutes or more per week of moderate-intensity aerobic exercise or about seventy-five minutes per week of vigorous-intensity aerobic activity (O'Keefe et al. 2018). But there's a catch. Note: in the following picture (Pic. 22 on the next page), the heart risk goes up—yes, up—if exercising daily. When it comes to activity, taking breaks matters. This is something I explored in Chapter 6 when looking at sleep's impact on just right.

What to make of all this information? Sure, I can monitor my exercise time, but steroid levels or confidence are not easy to quantify. Is that what self-help is about, just accumulating numbers in the search for excellence? Yes and no.

Our cellular selves have their own reflexive way of just right, which is something we learned in Chapter 5. We can try choosing to pursue knowledge and health, but it's just as

Exercise

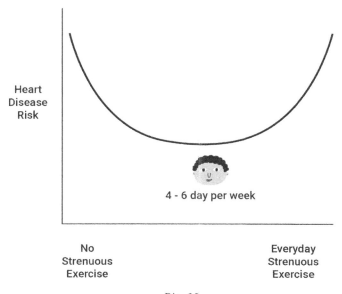

Heart Disease Risk

4 - 6 day per week

No Strenuous Exercise

Everyday Strenuous Exercise

Pic. 22.

important to know we are preconditioned toward finding just right at a cellular level. This is Stan's body finding its way back to equilibrium once a healthy raspberry baseline was established.

On the other hand, Stan was intentional, and it's clear that leaving space for despair, suffering, and stress has a way of driving performance. That type of space to improve requires paying attention—real attention—getting clear and knowing how we get in our own way. Just right self-help, as the cliché goes, may be as simple as "know thyself."

I knew to fully understand Stan's discomfort, I needed to examine my own. If I'm going to hold up a mirror to people like him, it's best I prop that mirror up on the wall and shine it on myself—even if it makes me uncomfortable along the way. Let's go know thyself about thyself.

I've been mildly allergic to the term self-help for as long as I can remember. I think the rebellion comes from my bias that improvement is mechanical and overly prescriptive, like a recipe for cake you just bake up and "ding!" you're this super-human who's got it all figured out. Yuck. I'd rather figure it out on my own if that's the process, thank you.

It could also just be semantics. I like the term rituals, but shy away from using habits. I like the term exercise but shy away from saying working out. My allergy doesn't cut across all categories either; I feel programs such as twelve-step and Al-Anon are wonderful and transformative. I just don't want the pursuit of some version of better to feel inauthentic or overly dogmatic.

I think people holding up mirrors, like the one Stan received, can be useful for those who are ready to see more clearly. Let them find their good side and pop their collar if that's how they like it. It's up to them to move around and nudge them to take a closer look.

As a kid, I could have benefited from knowing more about how competence related to confidence or what the overproduction of steroids may be doing to my health. I generally lacked confidence and suspect my body's steroid levels were chronically high due to being overly sensitive to other peoples' opinions. The mirror that was held up for me would benefit from someone who affirmed my best instincts.

As a youth, self-help sometimes felt more like self-survival. I remember planning my adolescent school days avoiding certain school hallways with the goal of avoiding the brutes, with fear being my most reliable help. All this resulted in being wary and extremely interested in not being noticed. It was the beginning of my relationship with impostor syndrome, which still lives to this day. Thankfully, examining this tendency closer over the years has made it less complex and more familiar.

When the feeling of just right hit me growing up, the sweet—and albeit brief—rewards were earned mostly by sweat and labor. Self-help came in the form of an exam score or a new skill. It was grit before the term was popular. As my body physically caught up, I didn't mind as much being noticed for things I was getting better at. But my relationship with the fear of being "found out" did not. I wasn't familiar with myself well enough to even know what it was. What teenager really is though? The silver lining of growing old is the clarity that comes with perspective.

Friedrich Nietzsche once said, "There are no facts, only interpretations."

I don't believe that's true, but I'm convinced more and more interpretations matter the most. The stories we tell ourselves about our lives come from strange wellsprings. To get the best interpretation, search for good people holding up good mirrors with an appropriate number of good nudges. Let intuition be just as helpful as numbers. That's the only self-help advice I can give to know oneself better.

Having only scratched the surface of self-help, there is a sense that the discussion feels incomplete. How can offering a few specific examples of U-shaped curves have applicability across a topic as vast and broad as self-improvement?

My hope is the relationships between confidence/competence and stress/performance can be applied across a wide spectrum of personal searches. Whether it's learning how to sew, getting a promotion, or dribbling a basketball, mastering the "hard skill" serves to complement "the soft skill" these perspectives offer. They also serve as an anchor toward finding tactics that work, whether that's cold showers, meditation, a spin class, or knowing oneself well enough to trust one's intuition. In the end, trusting the mirror and the person holding it probably matters most.

Searching for just right is in the doing, but more importantly, it's in the clarity that comes from the doing. Our next stop in the just right search is in an area where we humans do a lot of doing: the environment. Understanding this word more clearly has implications in the search for our relationship to facts, feelings, and the relationship between the two. Let's take a look at how we can help ourselves better understand its impact all around us.

CHAPTER 10
ENVIRONMENT—A RELATIONSHIP TO FACTS, FEELINGS, AND CONTROL

Nature does not hurry, yet everything is accomplished.

—LAO TZU

The word environment conjures up many ideas, making any "just right" search difficult. At its most basic, environment simply refers to the objects, conditions, and circumstances that surround us. Modern times and human impact have forced us to look at the environment in a completely new context. I doubt my caveman ancestors were thinking about their carbon footprint ten thousand years ago. Now it's being suggested as the morally right thing to do.

This will not be an exercise in doom and gloom. I have confidence humans are collectively capable of appreciating the almost magical power the environment has over us. The foresight of the United States to make Yellowstone the world's first national park in 1872 was born out of understanding that power (National Park Service 2020). The worry comes at where we're trending.

While we have a capacity for primal connection to the conditions around us, the modern world now threatens that connection in the most consequential ways. Spend too much time in front of a screen and see how connected we feel. Not a day goes by that we don't add images of polar bears, melting ice caps, electric car ads, or documentaries on sea levels rising to our headspace. Modern times mean more curated images of the environment than the actual environment. The environment looks better through the filters on our phones.

All this begs the question: if the environment is so important, why can it be so difficult to search for a just right perspective on it?

As I've aged, I've come to understand my own right search on the environment on three levels. They will be the foundation for what is to come. My hope is they inform critical thinking about our surroundings. Simply put, the three levels are:

1. the facts,

2. my feelings on those facts, and

3. my relationship to the surroundings.

The modern times we live in influence the first two. The last is me at my most primal.

And what does most primal mean? It's coming to understand the control we have, the control we don't, and our relationship with both categories. Our environment has plenty to teach us about control, whether it's thinking about how angry, sad, or filled with joy I am about my surroundings. Any environmental emotion seems tethered to this control instinct.

This chapter will be an exploration of facts, feeling on facts, and our surroundings. The search for just right is about coming to a reasonable understanding with all three levels. The search for just right in this chapter will be more fundamentally about a primal relationship with control. It's getting a deeper truth about facts and feelings.

This chapter will take some strange turns, but we're used to that now. It will explore a story of one person's very personal relationship to his environment. It will also explore the power that storytelling has to teach about control and our connection to the world. We will look at America's relationship to facts, feelings, and the power struggle over the belief systems about the environment. Some of the ideas explored will seem familiar to the ones discussed in Chapter 3. Finally, it will be marveling at the power of water and how appreciating its properties within and all around us can ground us. Okay, enough summarizing, let's go meet Roger, someone at a crossroads with his environment and the notion of control.

After meeting Roger several times, it became clear something in his environment was off. That picture was not obvious at the beginning. Sometimes, conversations need to marinate to realize what exactly we're searching for.

To the outside world, Roger appeared healthy, even robust—sturdy frame, newly retired, a hunter, woodworker, and active grandparent. He wore Carhartt pants and boots with a Vikings cap and had a two-day stubble. He was easygoing and talkative. It was clear I wasn't going to have to dig for information. The question was what information I'd get from him.

While I was happy to break down the Minnesota Vikings' offensive line problems, I knew he hadn't come to ask me to be an amateur NFL offensive coordinator. Someone warned me this may happen. I'd met his wife, who'd encouraged him to see me. She tipped me off to his chatty nature.

Finally, we got to the business of his concerns. I asked him where he wanted to start.

"I'm struggling with breathing. It's getting harder and harder to keep up with my grandkids."

I looked at his record. He'd seen a lung specialist for his asthma in the past year and done the requisite tests. Despite that, he'd needed several rounds of steroids in the past year to get his wheezing and coughing under control.

I asked him if he'd followed up with his specialist. He had not. I told him we needed to make that a priority.

He'd brought in his inhaler, so I asked him to show me how he used it. We made some modifications to his technique, but I wasn't confident this fixed everything.

As we finished the teaching, I had a flashback of his spouse, who'd I'd also seen. I realized she suffered from these same problems. I was also curious about what he was cooking up in his woodshop.

"Tell me a little about your home and woodworking shop. Have you had any air quality problems before?" I asked.

"Well, it's a typical old Minneapolis home. It's pretty closed off. My woodworking shop is in the garage," he said.

"Do you get good air coming through when you're working?"

"During the summer, yes, because I can keep the doors open. But the dust is pretty bad in the winter. I open up the garage during off times. But when I'm in there in January, it's pretty sealed off. It's too damn cold."

"Is your wife in there much?" I asked.

"No, no, no," he replied, surprised I'd even consider the question. "She steers clear of that area. That's my man cave."

"Any prior water damage in the home? Any chances for mold to grow or develop?"

"I've had water in the basement a couple of times. I think that's common for most people," he said. "I've seen a few things growing in the basement, but nothing crazy. Frankly, we're never down there other than to fetch a box of supplies."

At this point, I shared my concern about the environment contributing to his symptoms. I shared the connection I saw between him and his spouse's picture: the inhalers that didn't seem to work just right, the use of the steroids, the wheezing.

He thought about it for a second, a look of revelation coming across his face.

"Yeah, we do have the same breathing problems. We're both on that darn nebulizer machine like a bunch of addicts. We use our inhalers like we're smoking buddies. Yeah, something doesn't add up."

I told him why I thought the issue may not be the medicines but instead his environment.

He looked at me with the sense I get from patients at times. It's a look that says, "Yeah, you might be right, but the fix sounds *really* hard, *really* inconvenient, and *really* expensive."

Getting to the bottom of things can reveal inconvenient truths—inconvenient truths inspiring dread and rubbing up against what's in our control.

We left the meeting fine-tuning his asthma plan a bit, increasing his inhaler dose, and hoping his inhaler technique would improve his symptoms. These were things that were simple and easy to do. We were hopeful it might make some difference around the margins.

I had my doubts.

As I headed back to my desk, I talked with a student learner who had seen Roger with me. He buzzed the way learners sometimes do when an answer may be outside the textbook they bury themselves in. He had never pondered air quality or environmental exposure before.

I assigned the student the task of looking up the air quality standards in Roger's neighborhood relative to the rest of the state. This was publicly available information. We also started looking at how water damage and working in an unventilated woodworking space could impact someone's respiratory picture.

What came up confirmed our suspicions. Roger's zip code had the poorest air quality in the state. His unventilated woodworking shop could leave particulates in the air that could worsen his symptoms, even if he is wearing a mask. We realized if he had any type of visible mold growing downstairs, respiratory symptoms for those sensitive to it could make it worse.

This was three potential strikes against Roger and his wife's breathing situation.

Knowing I couldn't ask Roger to move, I called him with a plan to look at ventilating his shop and getting services out to the home to look for any visible basement mold. He said he would. I hoped, for his sake, he looked at his environment closer.

Roger messaged me some months later to say he was still struggling. I asked if he'd looked at his home closer. He said he hadn't but promised he would when hunting season was over. I realized in that moment how little control I had to make his situation whole. I somehow realized the relationship to control what ailed Roger now was afflicting me.

Roger's relationship with his own environment and control over it are worth exploring. Let's explore the post primal relationship to his surroundings first. Air quality in a large city is beyond any one person's control. Moving outside the city wasn't an option for him, presumably because his grandkids were nearby. The cost of water damage in a home or installing a ventilation system in a garage can be expensive. Some people don't have the financial means to go through that type of remodeling or the cost of a move after retirement. It's easy to get discouraged even if some notion of control feels possible, even if it's small.

Then there are the facts: we don't know the exact environmental impact of any water damage or air particulates in Roger's home. That requires expertise to examine and often comes at a price, which can add to the futility. How do we know our direction when we don't have a complete set of facts? It's easy to have more negative feelings as the dollars add up or the lack of certainty.

Even if certainty isn't an option, there is an understanding we can seek to better understand our environment. For example, there are more than one thousand different identified home molds (National Center for Healthy Housing 2022). Some studies cite home mold rates as high as 70 percent (Drah 2022). Many of us can coexist with these microbes, unaware of their often-invisible presence.

Online, my student and I were able to find air quality information published by the state. Add that to the fact that two people lived in the same house with the same respiratory problems, and it's not much of a leap to assume something isn't right.

Although examining Roger's facts—air quality, mold—feelings—frustration, futility—and sense of control—family connection to neighborhood, finances—can be helpful in understanding our personal relationship to the environment, a more holistic just right perspective requires a different approach. That means stepping away from the control we accept from reality and taking a sharp right turn to science fiction. Science fiction? Yes, science fiction! Stay with me here, even if science fiction isn't your cup of tea.

Dystopian storytelling is ripe with examples of humans turning knowledge bits—say air quality—into plans to exert control over the environment—say a man-made gas that allows for thought control. This often occurs to our human peril. The examples from popular culture are endless: *The Terminator* (Sky Net), *Star Wars* (Death Star), *The Matrix* (robot overlords harvesting humans). And I'm just naming some of the most obvious ones in movies. Pull up Netflix sometime and count the science fiction. It's a common way we come to understand control through storytelling.

To better understand this form of instructive storytelling, I want to go back to the very first credited piece of science fiction (History.com 2019). It's a story of relationships and hubris and what goes wrong when we try to separate the ways we humans interact with our environment. No, we are not Goldilocks in the forest anymore. We are in a story of what it means to be alive!

Written in 1818 by the English author Mary Shelley, *The Story of Frankenstein* chronicles the life of Victor Frankenstein, a scientist who sets out to make a creature of unbridled abilities. Young Victor is talented but grief-stricken after his mother dies of scarlet fever just before he leaves for university. It's this Victor who sets out to make his mark on the world in an unprecedented way.

To cope with his sadness, he works tirelessly on his studies, in particular the sciences. His efforts and interest lead him to an amazing discovery: a way to impart life into non-living matter. He sets out to make a humanoid-like creature using this technology, an eight-foot-tall male with physical beauty and abundant talents. The possibilities with this revelation feel endless.

Many know what happens next. The creature takes on appalling features during the animation process, where the famous "It's alive!" phrase is uttered. Young Victor is stunned at the sight of him and runs. Victor returns only to find the creature has disappeared. Victor then falls ill and recovers slowly, only to find out months later the creature killed his brother William and successfully framed William's nanny, Justine, for the crime.

After the interaction between Frankenstein and the creature, things only get worse—think gas lighting before the colloquialism existed.

The creature demands Victor make him a female partner, threatening the lives of the people around him. Victor obliges, then gives up on the experiment, knowing it would only make things worse. The creature then kills Victor's friend and frames him for the murder. He is exonerated but has his wife, Elizabeth, killed by the creature shortly after their marriage. A manhunt begins as Victor unsuccessfully chases the creature far and wide. Victor dies of exhaustion in vain. The creature feels only sadness and regret for the carnage he's created, vowing to kill himself as he floats away during the final scenes.

The end.

The Story of Frankenstein reveals a relationship to one's environment gone wrong. On a human level, I get it. Victor's discovery of an ability to impart life where it didn't exist must have felt intoxicating. The power and control to shape an environment is endless. And being a male in his early twenties probably didn't help. Note: If you're in your twenties and reading this, no offense, this will make sense as you get older.

But the control is an illusion. Young Victor feels he can control everything in the process, until he can't. His attempts to further control the situation continue to fail. It's a story of hubris and tragedy, with Victor stumbling after some form of control. Its powerful lessons are repeated in other science fiction stories. It's like we can't get enough of humans making a mess of things with an unhealthy relationship to power and control.

Victor is so broken at the end that he utters to seek "happiness in tranquility and avoid ambition." It may be misguided to avoid ambition. But blind ambition is the catnip for the illusion of complete control.

I like *The Story of Frankenstein* for many reasons.[16] The author Mary Shelley is ambiguous with the mechanics of the invention but not its power. It also forces me to zoom out and think about my relationship to facts and control in any environment.

The "It's alive" phrase is popular because it captures a way of expressing a relatable unbridled delusional joy. It's storytelling showing how an unhealthy relationship with control leads to an imbalanced relationship to our environment.

---

16   Duh. You included it in a book.

Death and mayhem ensue. It seems like a good teaching but have we heeded the lessons?

With Roger, our person with difficulty breathing, there was no sense of control. With young Victor, there was a sense that complete control was possible. Is there some way to find a just right somewhere? The answer is muddled, but it's helpful to look at another example where facts, feelings, and control once again take center stage.

Regarding facts about the mother earth version of the environment, these are strange times. Never has it been easier to gather them. Never has it been harder for our society to agree on a common set of them. A quick search of the World Health Organization (WHO) shows endless categories of information on everything from water safety to pandemic responses. While American trust in the WHO remains relatively strong, that trust seems to vary depending on political affiliation (Bayram and Shields 2021).

A survey question from the Pew Research Center in 2020 explains this well. It shows that "about seven-in-ten Democrats (72 percent) say human activity contributes a great deal to climate change, compared with roughly two-in-ten Republicans (22 percent), a difference of fifty percentage points."

I wonder if it's the "human activity" and "great deal" part of the question that drives the stark disparity. But I wonder more if we are collectively in search of facts that fit our beliefs rather than the other way around. Remember, there are facts, feelings, and control. If feelings are to take up too much room, there isn't much left for facts to weigh in.

With our collective reliance on institutional structures in question, we'd be wise to remind ourselves that the facts we hear—and the experts who share them—are anchored in trust. And it appears our environment is clouded with the wariness that everybody has an agenda, off to find their own fact factions to define "human activity" and "great deal." Wariness is what comes when control feels like it's in the balance. This misconception with facts—often in numbers—was a subject we explored in Chapter 3. Context and presentation can mean everything, as does our relationship with expertise.

The idea of balance—or just right—is the fundamental theme that's come up over and over in the book. What has hopefully become clear is this: when we're looking too close through the microscope, it's time to give that thing some distance. When we're looking into the horizon with our eyes permanently squinted, it's time to grab the binoculars.

What we need is going to vary. For young Victor Frankenstein, it's using a trusted mentor in addition to his microscope to assure blind ambition and joy don't lead to something more sinister. For Roger, it's seeing there are resources to help him get to the root of the problem, even if those resources may be hard to implement. To allow somebody with binoculars to help him see some sort of control is within his grasp.

The public debate on the environment is more complicated—there's a shocker—requiring both the microscope and the binoculars. Who gets handed what requires individuals to state their understanding of the facts, what feelings those facts invoke, and what sense of control is being lost or gained. Nothing short of a collective reckoning with reality will help save our environment from human hubris. That and the perspective we control whether the planet stays "alive" or not.

Beyond the debates on there are a lot of places to go, but I'm going to veer toward a more fundamental element in our environment. This is looking closer at something most of us take for granted: water. By seeing its power all around us, it can further strengthen the responsibility to take care of what's within us.

What better environmental aspect of life to explore than water, one of the most abundant of Earth's resources and arguably its most important.

"Water is the driving force of all nature."

—LEONARDO DA VINCI

Another smart guy with a smart perspective. That force is a literal just right within and all around us.

Gaining a deeper understanding of water in a few paragraphs without sounding like an over-caffeinated high school science teacher or Doc Brown from the movie *Back the Future*—second Doc Brown reference!—is difficult, but I'll try. Water is amazing. It takes on various states of solid, liquid, and gas at temperatures and pressure we can measure. The melting numbers of thirty-two degrees Fahrenheit and zero degrees Celsius—at the right atmospheric pressure—are two of the most commonly understood in all of science.

Water is critical, not just for drinking. It's needed in just right amounts for habitat and atmospheric temperature control. Water can take on different shapes and properties depending on the introduction of different compounds like sodium chloride—salt. It dissolves things, transports things, energizes things, helps feed things, and thirty other critical things I'm leaving out. All of these are in a constant state of renewal and regeneration.

While we have propped water up in science, religion, and song, humans are water's nemesis, attempting, through hubris, to throw off that just right balance it has established with our Earth (Haddeland et al. 2013). The numbers tell us that.

In Chapter 1, I spoke with awe and reverence that the earth resides in the "not too hot, not too cold" Goldilocks zone necessary for life on Earth. This is more than just the earth's distance from the sun but is tied to something called the greenhouse effect. Many have heard of it, but not as many understand what it means.

Time for more Doc Brown science teacher talk.

The greenhouse effect is a process that occurs when gases in the earth's atmosphere trap the sun's heat (NASA 2022). Pic. 23 on page 175 shows how this works. It's the same thing that happens anytime you walk into an indoor greenhouse, except on a much larger scale. The greenhouse effect makes Earth much warmer and is a foundational just right on par with our distance from the sun. There are multiple factors that go into the greenhouse effects, with carbon dioxide getting the headlines due to the debate on the human impact—and rightfully so. But water vapor is Earth's most abundant greenhouse gas. It's responsible for about half of Earth's greenhouse effect (Buis 2022). Without it, we'd be shivering messes.

All this is to say that anything that's impacting water is worth taking action on. It's clear, water is changing on this planet, a common fact that is anchored in science and the people who produce it. To those who don't want to see the science, or believe humans are the cause, or even squabble

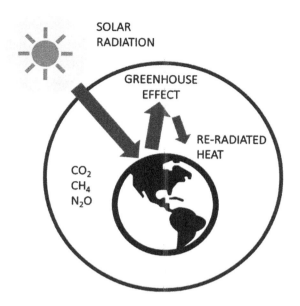

Pic. 23.

about how facts become anchored to an agenda, just look up when it starts to rain. Realize what we stand to lose if we don't nurture it. Realize our creations can turn out like young Victor Frankenstein if we don't take a moment to reflect on where hubris can get us.

Strange turns indeed! Our relationship to the word environment takes on so many dimensions. Hopefully, the notion of objects and surroundings took on greater meetings in our examples of Roger, Victor Frankenstein, and water. It's hard to reconcile all these in one message.

In Chapter 2, we got to explore four meanings—courage, intuition, essence, digestion—that we could all somewhat coherently appreciate. With environment, the just right search is much more relational; it is an appreciation of facts, feelings, and the relationship between them that helps us understand our relationship to control. This relationship to control—the notion that we look back when we're too close and look close when we're too far back—is tricky. There's no perfect formula to do either. Often, it takes the perspective of others or a sense our intuition is giving us that something isn't right.

Our planet needs us to live not in righteousness or denial. It needs us to find a way to relate to our surroundings and feel the rain on our face and the wind at our back. We need to wake up to the precarious nature of the gifts we have that will keep us alive and enjoy.

Where we're heading next will be about facts, feelings, and control on some fundamental just rights about death and religion. We'll see where just right lives in tensions between concepts like conviction and doubt. We've been building toward these existential topics. Let's explore how we relate better to the beyond.

PART 3

GOLDILOCKS AND THE BEYOND

CHAPTER 11

RELIGION—AN EXAMINATION INTO THE NATURE OF CONVICTION AND DOUBT

In the 2007 movie *Spider-Man 3*, Peter Parker—also known as Spider-Man—is at a crossroads. His antagonist, Eddie Brock—also known as Venom—uses the press to spread misinformation and frames Peter as an evil menace. To confront his accuser, Peter decides to hurt Eddie not with punches—that comes later in the movie—but by delivering the famous line:

"You want forgiveness? Get religion."

This line was poignant as earlier, Eddie's character prayed for Spider-Man's demise. It was a classic superhero meets cowboy western with a side of rhetorical philosophy thrown in. Peter didn't even give the dumbfounded Eddie a chance to respond, knowing all he had to do was drop the mic and walk away.

As I explored earlier, how cool would it be to have just the right line to deliver at just the right moment? To drop the mic and hit some magic slow-motion button, just like our smartphones. Maybe I watch too much TV.

For me, the word "get" makes this line sing, in part because of its two meanings—both of which Peter seems to play off Eddie. The first is the way we think about "get" as a means of obtaining something, like milk from the store or gas for our cars. In some ways, we do "get" religion this way, whether it's through beautiful art; donating our time, talent, and treasure to an institution; admiring impressive architecture; or being entranced with rituals. Its religion consumed through the pleasant sensory experiences that a place of worship can sometimes invoke. It can also feel transactional.

The other version of "get" is a little different. It's a version where the goal is more "aha!" and the meaning clicks into place. This is sitting in the pews, hearing the sermon or reading the text and having a phrase strike you in just the right way. This is when you feel a sense of awe, empathy, or wonder. The former version is interesting but not the subject of this chapter. We will be exploring more of the latter "aha!" meaning as it speaks to the push and pull underpinnings of any religion: faith. Understanding faith, this idea that comes with feelings of conviction and doubt, are the seeds of searching for a just right.

It's no surprise that religion is a challenging subject to understand in the just right framework. I've struggled to reconcile its importance as its sway, at least in the traditional sense, seems to be dwindling. Research shows more and more Americans are opting out of formal religion altogether (Smith 2021). Is this a sign that they're not searching for existential meaning at all? Or is it that formal religion doesn't help in the search? Maybe scandal, relationship, or personal events early in life led to the disconnection? Given religion's relationship to conviction, faith, and doubt, it seemed important to search for some understanding.

A Pew research study in 2021 quantifies this dwindling shift in more detail. About three-in-ten people—29 percent—now classify themselves as religious "nones"—atheists, agnostics, or "nothing in particular"—when asked about their religious identity. This compares to 16 percent in 2007. There has been a 15 percent decline in that same 2007 to 2021 time period in people describing religion as "very important in their lives." There's also been a 10 percent decline in daily prayer. Taken together, a national trend appears. All that said, most Americans still classify themselves as religious. How do we reconcile this trend with religion's importance in our everyday lives? And further, what does it mean if this trend continues?

Many academics and political scientists have attempted to explain the trend and, as is typical in academia, their explanations vary (Boorstein 2022). Some researchers focus on the anti-religion sentiments that exist within secular groups, resulting in less religious engagement overall. Others focus on how people moving toward a more secular worldview don't fit into nice categories and may not want to be labeled Baptist, Lutheran, or Hindu, so they choose nothing when asked. Still others describe a general ambivalence toward religion while still holding strong views—or faith?—on free-thinking and science. What seems clear is the unclear: the search for a just right framework of American sentiment leaves more questions than answers. Does less religion mean less existential conviction, doubt, and faith? Or has a collective existential ambivalence now settled in?

The answers to these questions are best explored through the push and pull of Peter Parker's—I mean Spider-Man's—second "aha!" version of how we "get" religion. This doesn't come from commentaries on secularization data but from deep conversations into the muddy realities of our family origins of conviction, doubt, fear, and faith. It's zooming into our lives, then backing up and asking for how religion helps with faith. It's the best way to "get" religion.

What I've found along the way will seem both obvious and easy to forget. It goes something like this: individuals with the most conviction help those with the most doubt challenge their understandings. Individuals with the most doubt offer the convicted the opportunity to examine their conviction more clearly. The convicted help doubters see hope is possible as an alternative to ambivalence and futility. Both help one another in the search for just right.

Conviction and doubt are best framed as a tug-of-war that builds strength for the other. If one is open to the strength and suffering to come, a search is possible, and the war continues. If one is closed off, the game eventually ends, and nobody stands to build anything. The rope just lies there and a staring contest—at best—or screaming match—at worst—ensues.

I find conviction and doubt in many places, and Maria's story is that exploration turned up full blast. It's pure conviction clobbering me into confronting strong feelings in quick order. If I stayed open and continued to hang onto the rope, I knew it had a lot to offer me as a means to a better understanding of faith and saying "aha!" Hopefully, it does the same for you.

Maria is an example of someone with clear conviction, faith, and zero doubts. I was not in search of a discussion about faith and religion when we met. Fortunately—with the benefit of hindsight—Maria had other plans for me.

They asked me to talk to Maria about her sleeping difficulties. In her early eighties, she was taking three different sleep medications, something that may sound similar to Gus from Chapter 5. The two couldn't have been more different. Maria was experiencing memory problems, likely made worse by medicines, with the added challenge of being aware of this mental change. She was also running into objects at all hours of the night with little concern, rising at 3 a.m. to pray for the souls of the unsaved, even if that meant banging into doorways along the way.

My job was to talk to her about risk, hopefully, to help her gain some insight and start the process of reducing her dependence on medications. Her family, who asked me to come in, was concerned about her well-being, even if she wasn't. I knew I had my work cut out for me thirty seconds into our sit-down.

"Have you thought about burning in hell and needing to be saved?" she asked me after I told her my role.

"I have not," I told her, too dumbfounded to say anything else.

"Your soul needs saving. We need not talk about my sleep or my medicines. They are fine. What I fear is that you need to take up the Lord as your Savior."

Her questions then started rapid fire. I was playing defense. She asked me about Jesus, about the New Testament, about where I grew up, about what scripture verses I knew. Wasn't I the one hired to ask the questions? It was clear this lady *really* meant soul saving. She was wasting no time. I needed to gain some conversational footing.

"I think these questions are coming from a good place. But they aren't part of what I'm asked to help you with now.

Can we talk about your health? At the end, if there is time, I will discuss these matters with you," I said.

I figured a delay was my only way out, the conversational boundaries way off course. She agreed.

I got her to explain her routine. Three sleep medicines at 11 p.m. Bedtime at midnight. Alarm clocks off at 3 a.m. to pray in the next room if the medication-induced disorientation wasn't too strong. Back to bed at 4 a.m. Wake up again at 7 a.m., back to bed around 10 a.m., rising throughout to "barely function" as she put it.

I got her to admit her life had become smaller. She acknowledged her spouse and family were worried about her health.

It was all making sense. I got the conversional soul-saving blitzkrieg because I was one of the few new people to recently enter her life. She'd been training for me, her world so small now that any souls status became fertile ground for her message. I decided to it was time to grab the rope and engage in Maria's tug-of-war.

The rest of our conversation veered into strange territory. She agreed to stop one of her sleep medicines. I took that as a small win. She spent ten minutes quoting Bible verses she'd committed to memory to show that the medicines were not having the negative impact on her memory that her family claimed. I countered that her balance and running into walls at 3 a.m. was my primary concern right now, not her memory. I was faithful that her safety at home was the most critical.

It went on like this, religion and pharmacology tugging back and forth, two parallel conversations seemingly miles apart but versions of convictions, doubt, and faith right in front of us. I started to wonder if this is why the more disorienting conversations leave their lasting marks on us, their novelty a way of pushing against the force of familiarity we come to expect.

In the end, my appeal to her family and their welfare seemed like my only hope. In a moment of frank honesty, I told her she was a woman with religious clarity, and that clarity had closed her off to the people she cared most about. I even surprised myself that I'd say something like that to a perfect stranger I'd met just forty-five minutes ago. She acknowledged the point, even if she seemed ambivalent about changing. I think she appreciated by my conviction as she finally agreed to change her medicines "over time." In a twist, my parallel conviction had made her doubt her own ambivalence to sleeping medications.

We left the conversation amicably. She said she'd pray for me. I told her I appreciated the sentiment.

I realized after we parted ways that I had encountered someone who awakened my own dormant doubts, a tug-of-war where my muscles were in serious need of conditioning. Conversations with people like Maria offer an opportunity to understand the tug-of-war further. The question was whether I'd grab the rope.

Maria's story, or at least a version of it, is familiar for many of us. We are in a conversation with someone we just met. That conversation is going along just fine, but then out of nowhere that something gets discarded, and a deep intense conversation about religion mysteriously breaks out. Maybe this has happened at your front door when a stranger knocks. Sometimes it happens at work. Or maybe it's at the family get-together when an aunt or uncle seems to come equipped with only a one-track religious mind. The point is that we get pulled into these situations, whether we like it or not. The game of tug-of-war will find us, even if it's a game we try to avoid.

The natural reflex, at least for me, has been to recoil in these moments. But it's become apparent over time that I'm missing something. Even if the conversation isn't what we want or expect, its novelty is too bright, its importance to getting to the "aha" version of understanding is. It's grabbing the rope and hanging on, with the faith that strength and suffering will come.

When I met Maria, there was another reflex that kicked in: how exactly did she get to this point? What makes her so convicted? Or me so doubtful? Was she made in a lab somewhere? Or dipped in a special religious mental clarity oil? The most convicted and the strongest doubters offer us the gift of having us stand up at attention and notice. The Marias of the world tell us the game is on, and the stakes are high.

I mentioned earlier how we often wrap the seeds of our relationship to conviction, doubt, and faith in our origin story. If her family hadn't tasked me with helping Maria avoid falling into doorways, I probably would have spent hours asking her how she arrived at such convictions. Maybe I would have gotten there after her concern for my soul's fate had subsided. It's hard to say, as our time together was relatively short.

After meeting Maria, I decided I needed to "get religion" to examine the origin story of my tug-of-war. It meant reckoning with the times I grabbed the rope and when I let go. Or where did the rope lie now?

Like many kids, my parents raised me in an organized religion. Being religious seems to come with its own inertia toward conviction, where the tug of doubt is hidden from view. I had a very Catholic childhood as far as these things go: weekly Sunday mass, attending religion class on Wednesday nights. The notorious Catholic guilt was cooked into me at an early age medium-well. I was expected to learn prayers. I was expected to go to reconciliation and learn to confess sins, even if the sin was only a thought of playground revenge—in Catholicism, impure thoughts were still necessary to purge and expunge. To be a "good Catholic," you were expected to be a "good kid." Being a good kid meant following rules. Following rules came pretty easy to me, so being a "good Catholic" and "good kid" was off to a good start.

Being Catholic meant many developmental milestones: receiving Eucharist at age eight, even if the transfiguration to the body and blood of Christ grossed me out and going through confirmation—the coming-of-age process of becoming a religious "adult"—as an adolescent. I was on a Christian conveyor belt, and I didn't question getting dumped into the pew of other obedient churchgoers. Remember, I was a "good kid." When I was thirteen, there was a rumor started by a classmate that I wanted to become a priest. This even got the popular girls intrigued, one of them came up to me to ask if it was true.

"I don't know," was all I could say.

I felt hot sweat come across my face, tinged with embarrassment. Was I that boring and "good" that this is how I got noticed or stood out? I thought about how cute she was and how weird it was to get noticed for something that I knew meant celibacy. I knew it wasn't very "good" or Catholic on such things. I also knew she'd never go for a boy three inches shorter than she was who was developmentally closer to ten. Being thirteen and in doubt about the priesthood but convicted on the power of romantic attraction threw me for a loop. It was a sign of things to come.

I'd like to say the priest rumor stopped with the cute girl, but it didn't. Somehow it found its way to my grandmother as if blown by sacred winds ten miles east. Visits to my grandmother in high school usually came with a clergy question. To my grandmother, a grandson becoming a priest was a better version of Dean Martin or Frank Sinatra entering the home. Being from a big family, I had many male cousins. Was I the only one she hung hopes of the priestly collar on?

As I moved into young adulthood, the Catholic conveyor belt's power kept me in the pews. While the doubts lingered, they were swatted away. The thoughts of cute girls were not. I sang the songs and listened to the sermons. I liked the hymns, even if I couldn't sing a lick. I liked the stories, at least the ones free from the dogma and the creeds. I liked the smell of incense, and I liked the power of church architecture to make grand statements. I also liked the community of going to church with my friends.

But as I made it to my midtwenties, the allure began to fade. I began to question everything. Doubt seeped in everywhere, the tug-of-war starting its own inertia where only conviction had previously lived. I started to read about other religions. I sought out the stories of Mohamed and Siddhartha and began to see connections with Jesus—maybe not in their details, but in the deeper truths they espoused. I started to explore Jesus as a man of his time, not just the sanitized version I had been presented.

I placed my exploration into doubt with another useful concept: perspective. A perspective that I was the beginning a new search. I could hold many different ideas up without strong conviction to any of them. Understanding my origin story, cute girls, grandmothers, priestly rumors and all, helped start this evolution of doubt that lives to this day.

Where I'm at now with faith is complicated. I'm a middle-aged man where doubts seem to come with more frequency than convictions. But I've come to embrace the tug-of-war and the confidence that comes with "getting" religion through the "aha!" version life offers, a moment that moves me a bit closer to faith. The child on the Catholic conveyor belt is gone, but that doesn't mean I don't mind finding myself in a pew from time to time. I move closer to faith, knowing clarity and conviction come in small servings. Now, my goal is to be fully present for it all. I am a man of faith in knowing answers get closer, but truth will never be fully realized.

Having heard Maria and my story, where does that leave us? Maybe to the streaming service offering *Spider-Man 3*? With the country turning more secular, with us hopefully turning to our origin stories to better understand our relationship to religion, conviction, doubt, and faith, how do we search for a version of just right? I mentioned the most convicted and biggest doubters have much to teach us, but I didn't offer how their relationship to death—the subject of Chapter 12—may inform another big lesson.

Come to find out, there is some evidence that having confidence or conviction in a religious belief, even if that confidence is atheism, may lead to less fear of death (Beres 2017). That is represented in the following inverted U-shaped curve in Pic. 24 below. Somehow leaning into the extremes, of being curious about how the Maria's got there, offers us a means of searching for tranquility where fear and angst normally lie.

It's instructive to imagine the ultra-convicted and ultra-doubters somehow finding an almost carefree—and maybe curious?—attitude at the end of life. It's not a U-shaped curve but a perfect circle of unity. It's something Maria, if I'd spent time talking to her about death, would have asked.

But fear of death isn't the only motivation to find a religious, spiritual, or faith home. People turn to religion for multiple reasons, whether that be community, security, solidarity, or control. As I've come to appreciate faith deeper, there is one conviction that I feel strongly resides in religion; it's that the tug-of-war lies in the common ways many religions move to the "aha" way of getting closer to the truth.

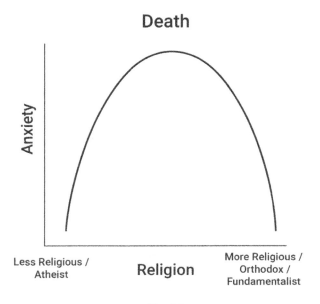

Pic. 24.

Religion is replete with similar examples of how to "get" religion. In Buddhism, the "middle way" instructs followers to avoid extremes of "sensual indulgence and self-mortification." The "middle way" is often seen as a phrase summarizing the Noble Eightfold Path central to the teachings of Siddhartha Gautama.

The Old and New Testament, as well as the Qur'an, are also full of examples and stories of moderation, equity, harmony, and equivalence. They speak of a middle way being free of rigidity of thought. Looking to God is the invitation to a moderate mindset. Satan is, by contrast, shown to be extravagant in mindset and a means of turning away from "getting" anything important.

Here are some quotes from religious texts that illustrate what I'm talking about:

- *You shall weigh with an equitable scale* (Qur'an 26:182).

- *You shall give the due alms to the relatives, the needy, the poor, and the traveling alien, but do not be excessive, extravagant* (Qur'an 17:26).

- *The Lord promotes equity and justice; the Lord's faithfulness extends throughout the earth* (Psa. 33:5).

- *Live in harmony with each other. Do not be arrogant but associate with humble people. Do not think that you are wiser than you really are* (Rom. 12:16).

Upon reflection, this makes sense. The duality expressed in the doubters and believers helps us in the struggle, whether or not they realize it.

Maria needed me to spread her conviction even if I didn't see clearly the same way she did. She responded to my conviction about her health, just as I needed her conviction to examine my doubts.

I needed to experience strong conviction and examine my origin story better as a means of understanding what faith is.

I needed Spider-Man to stand up to Venom and tell him to stop being a hater who leaves Venom in doubt.

Our search can happen just about anywhere, and hopefully, that gets us to somewhere closer to understanding faith. It's within our power and that gives me hope, something I trust is often one and the same.

CHAPTER 12

DEATH–COMPREHENDING THE MEASURABLE AND MYSTICAL

———

If you realize that all things change, there is nothing you will try to hold on to. If you are not afraid of dying, there is nothing you cannot achieve.

—LAO TZU

The author and philosopher Alan Watts certainly lived an interesting life. He was born in England and trained as an Episcopal priest. He was credited with bringing Indian and Chinese traditions of Buddhist, Taoist, and Hindu philosophy to a broader Western audience—in particular the United States—in the 1950s to 1960s (Alan Watts Organization 2022). He had a lot to say on a number of subjects, including the topic of death. Death is a challenging topic to discuss. I think Watt's perspective offers a "just right" way of viewing something most of us tend to look away from. It serves as a good launching point for what's coming.

In his speeches and writings, Watts spoke on the interplay between what he called the measurable and mystical views of the world (Mind Like the Sky 2013). He put those views and people into distinct camps. He labeled the measurable people as "prickly." To Watts, prickly people often cannot accept statements without a quantifiable way of representing them. To acknowledge otherwise is a form of intellectual sloth that stands in the way of human progress. Prickly people see matter and the world as distinct bits or particles to be counted and sorted as a way of determining the "truth" or next step forward. Progress depends on precision, and prickly people love logic and precision. Throughout this book, prickly people may be found in the research we've reviewed on sleep, nicotine, hypertension, and water—among other things. As you can probably guess by now, I'm a bit on the prickly side too.

Mystical people take a different point of view, according to Watts. He labeled mystics as seeing the world more as "goo," a strange word that is worth unpacking a bit. Goo people look at prickly people as understanding musical scales without recognizing how the notes move their soul. To goos, the world really is what Watt's called "wiggly lines."

Prickly people use logic and straight lines for truth, but this is a misunderstanding of the world for how it actually is. How many straight lines in nature does one actually see? Mountains, trees, and sand are all wiggly lines when you take enough time to notice.

Previously, we reviewed how numbers without context can lead to misconceptions. Goo people may tell prickly people that they're looking at the numbers without the proper context. And besides, according to the best science we have, doesn't matter sometimes act as both a particle and a wave (Sutter 2019)? For something like goo that is described as no shape, goo takes on the shape of many things. It takes the shape of ice cream and freshly baked chocolate chip cookies, and I like those. Goo is good!

At this point, you may be wondering: prickly? goo? wiggly? really? Was this philosopher creating some sort of new hippie language? The goal of his word choices is not clear to me. But it is clear he had a viewpoint that's worth taking note.

To Alan Watts, being prickly or goo is not an "either/or" binary proposition, but a point of view best appreciated on a spectrum. In that sense, the closer we move toward the measurable, the more it benefits shifting gears toward the mystical. The closer we move to the mystical, the more we need to look toward the measurable for answers. This nonbinary way of seeing things is a fundamental way to move toward right.

What does this have to do with death? I believe spending our days being both prickly and goo, much like matter acts as both particle and wave, can aid in our relationship with a topic we often associate with fear and pain. For example, death is both difficult and obvious; it is the thing that makes a mockery of everything else we spend our time doing. Understanding our relationship with death may be the most important thing we do in our brief time.

As we've outlined, storytelling is a powerful tool used to examine fundamental truths. This chapter will be no different. I hope it illuminates how the prickly and the goo seep into our day-to-day lives. After reading about Alec, hopefully, you'll appreciate where each of us swings along the measurable and mystical spectrum at any one time about matters of importance.

I've been meeting with Alec lately, a man on the cancer string. I've come to understand my conversations with advanced cancer patients in a category all their own; they feel both fast and slow, on their own spectrum. Slow in how conversations can take time to unfold, symptom after symptom, test after test. Fast in feeling, there are no wasted conversational moments. Why doesn't this happen all the time, the heightened sense of not wasting awareness? I find Alec a case study in the dance between the prickly and the goo: how the medical fight to keep us alive forces lots of prickly and how contemplating the beyond takes us into the goo.

Alec had all the conversational fast attributes. He'd been in chronic debilitating pain since being diagnosed with metastatic cancer a few months ago. He was remorseful because they didn't catch it earlier. He often swung between blaming himself and "the system." He smiles while telling me he's an "old hippie." He feels blaming "the man" comes easy. If it's easy, why not indulge his most basic instincts?

We get into other life details. He tells me how sad he is over recently losing his best friend to cancer. By cruel coincidence, he also shares his friend died of the same cancer he has now. Alec got his diagnosis just days after burying his friend. He wonders about the cosmic meaning of that coincidence, the greater meaning of it all. The goo has started.

He tells me more. He shares the crisis in spirit he has to fight on with his body struggling to go on. He's trying to stay present, but his mind keeps drifting toward the meaning of it all, about what it will be like when he dies. His ravaged body keeps reminding him time is short. He tells me he feels his mind floating in the clouds.

More goo—not his words—is starting to form all over our meeting. He knows I'm the drug guy, right? I wonder what lecture, podcast, or YouTube video I've come across that's prepared me for this. Nothing comes to mind. This feels like rabbi, priest, or shaman territory, not something where my skills are useful.

"I'm going to try and hang in there, whatever that means," he says at the end of his monologue.

We both let the meaning of "hang in there" hang in the conversation.

"I'm hoping your pain starts to get better," I tell him. "The cancer treatment can sometimes help with the bone pain."

He seems relieved to hear that.

It's hard for anyone to think about the big picture when their body is suffering. It's in our nature to make our point of view small, so we can survive. Despite the pain, he's about to shift toward his version of the big picture again.

"I miss my friend so much. I am trying to do yoga and meditate. I'm thinking of him while I do it, even though I know I shouldn't. I've done yoga my whole life. Now, this. I'm not sure what this all means."

What this means is me pivoting our big talk to his pain medication; all this goo is making me feel prickly. We review the muscle spasms up-and-down in his spine, the best ways to stay comfortable with medicines, and pain scores and goals. We talk cannabis. He tells me his dealer, on finding out his advanced cancer diagnosis, is now dropping off "freebies" to keep him more comfortable. We joke about drug dealers having hearts. He asks questions about the medical cannabis program as a way of going "legit." I find myself being pulled into the goo. I tell him to stick with the friends and family discount he's currently enjoying if that helps his state of mind.

More prickly starts to surface again. I now steer the conversation to the antidepressant he's taking. I confirm the dose. I can see he's going to run out in a few days. I know he forgets to fill medicines. More numbers. I tell him to go to the pharmacy and pick up the medicine, and that it will be ready in twenty-four hours. More numbers, numbers as truth. He says he will. I'm feeling good in my prickliness. He then takes me back again into the goo.

"I've been having these panic attacks. I feel alone. I am all alone in my apartment. I'm not sure who to talk to now that my friend is gone," he says, seemingly resigned to his fate.

I decide it's best I give into his goo.

We talk about his family. He has them, but they aren't regularly around. He hints at broken relationships but is coy with details. He spends most of his days in his apartment, alone to think about his suffering. We talk about getting out for walks—more goo. I suggest a "number of steps" walking goal for him—more prickly. We talk about sharing his sadness with a cancer support group to give his mind an outlet—more goo.

Our conversations go on like this. I get prickly about his blood pressure being too high, a side effect of his chemotherapy. He makes the medication adjustments I tell him to make and takes his blood pressure readings. I can get him to be prickly, but I'm dragging him there just as he's dragging me in the other direction.

I realize as death comes closer, prickly will not matter much to Alec. All the forces between Alec and I will continue to push us back and forth on the spectrum. What I realize is that maybe it's better for the both of us to engage in this push and pull. The equilibrium struck by this tug-of-war is another form of just right.

My conversation with Alec felt like a push and pull between two states of being.

What makes the push and pull between the mechanistic and mystical worldviews Alec and I had so disjointed is that temperamentally, we probably lean more toward one than the other. All of us have our limits.

The saddest version of goo for me are the people I meet who refer to themselves way too early in their lives in the past tense—some version of "I've had a good life" while they're far from being terminal. Looking back and being grateful is wonderful, but not seeing the now in a past tense, that's too gooey.

Like many things, I know a just right relationship with these ideas is complicated. Some of it may just be my disposition; being prickly just comes easier to me. Numbers, mechanisms, and calculations give me a sense of control. While it could be my nature, some of it may be nurture, a by-product of the measurable way they teach us to look at the body in medicine.

We divide the body into parts and create ologists for all of them—pulmonologist, nephrologist, gastroenterologists, cardiologist. These are some of the brightest, most caring, compassionate, and hardest working people one will ever encounter. They also mostly train to be prickly: to examine their organ, treat their organ, understand the evidence for their organ, and ground their words in logic and science. Most are good at it. The best of them add a side of goo to their prickly main course. Many save lives in a prickly state. In that sense, there is nothing inherently wrong with the approach. As I've come to learn, it's just incomplete.

To understand Alec's goo, I realized I needed to understand my own goo, a nod to the "know thyself" theme we explored earlier. Following is a story I debated even putting in the book, a decision I asked my wife to help me sort out. All she said was, "would you be honest to your work if you left it out?" Great question by an awfully smart person. I think you know the answer. I hope it reveals how incomplete things can feel.

I rushed into the twenty-week appointment just in time, and my wife was already waiting for me. It was the middle of a weekday, and a light snow had slowed my trip from work to the clinic. My wife sat in the waiting room chair, foot tapping up-and-down in the lobby. It had been a difficult pregnancy, no respite from fatigue, nausea, sadness, and soreness. She was miserable most of the time. The foot tapping wasn't pregnancy induced. This was how she normally operated in waiting rooms.

I could feel her anxiety as I sat down next to her. I sat down, said hello, and asked her how she was feeling. She told me how thankful she was that our two-year-old was being watched by her mother.

While I could sense her nerves, I had little of that feeling, and I was too self-involved to provide any comfort. I was excited; it would be our second child, something I had deeply wanted. We knew the plan was to see the sonographer first, get the pictures, then meet with the on-duty obstetrician afterward. I sensed things were going to go according to plan.

They escorted us to an exam room, and we assumed the positions, my wife Kerry on the table, me at her elbow opposite the sonographer's screen. We planned on learning the sex of the child. We found out we were having a girl. I felt elated.

What happened next changed everything.

I remember seeing a look on the sonographer's face. In my excitement, I developed a blind spot to notice something was gravely wrong. I had been told that sonographers, at least the good ones, know when something is wrong. Since they know, but can't say what they see, they have to put on a brave face because they are not "qualified"—whatever that means—to discuss the details.

I realize now there had been a crack in her expression. Remember, I was feeling a bit self-involved. I also know that all memories are reconstructed memories. Maybe I wanted to know something was wrong before that something wrong actually smacked me. Maybe we like to know when punches are coming. Being prickly, I wanted a logical answer, but I wasn't going to find one.

What happened next was a blur. We met with an obstetrician, not one we had normally met with during Kerry's first pregnancy. She was young and noticeably nervous, the messenger of the sobering news that our child was "very sick" with little other details. We left with several options: late pregnancy abortion, carrying the child out to term however that unfolded, or seeing a perinatologist and genetic counselor to give us clarity on a prognosis.

Given Kerry's physical misery, we knew we needed answers fast. It now made sense a suffering child was producing a suffering mother. We made an appointment for the perinatologist and genetic counselor for later that week.

We left the appointment stunned. I stupidly returned to work the next day to absorb in my prickly work while my wife suffered alone at home in goo with our son. In the three weeks that followed, the decision started ever so slowly to sort itself out. Our child was diagnosed with cytomegalovirus (CMV), a disease what would leave her severely disabled at best and dead at worst.

When we talked about bringing a severely disabled child into the world, both our minds were clouded. I had no choice but to contemplate the goo. For Kerry, the physical agony was enough to make any decisions fraught. During that time, she was having thoughts of self-harm, something I did not know until later. For me, all I wanted to do was run away from having to think about it, to find salvation in something prickly instead of just being present.

Looking back, all I see was my foolishness, how my default was nowhere near just right.

We visited the obstetrician again, where they reinforced the "your baby is very sick" and "there's nothing we can do" messages. Eventually, we had a discussion about whether this child would even survive at all. In a flurry of calls, we received two independent doctor reviews telling us our child would die either during birth or before it came to term. We then faced the biggest goo question of our lives: do you want to wait for this to happen naturally or go into the hospital and induce the pregnancy at twenty-four-and-a-half weeks?

Given how gravely ill Kerry was, we opted to induce. Everything that happened in the following days was goo. My body was going to slap me into a just right state, whether I liked it or not. This was me in a state of prickly withdrawal.

To complicate matters, I worked at the hospital where the induction would take place. Walking into the hospital, I felt the deepest need to be invisible. I remember Kerry's glazed expression as she delivered the baby, a picture of her absolute sadness mixed with absolute relief, a goo draining from her body.

After the delivery, they handed a wrapped one-and-a-half-pound baby girl to me. A cap was placed on her head as I rocked her nonbreathing body back and forth. I cracked, holding her in a way I can't even describe; a goo I've never felt before or since. It was my reintroduction to a deep goo, now as an adult. It made life a hell and worth living for all at once.

I stared at her features closely, knowing I'd get only these fleeting hello and goodbye moments. I felt my arms almost frozen as I handed her back to the nurse for cremation, a form of paralysis from sitting still and attentive for too long.

The prickly me feels the moment is akin to being in another dimension of reality. The hurt leaving a lasting mark in my nervous system in the absence of any physical injury. This is what trauma is.

I look at everything since that moment as helping me understand the goo more. Two additional miscarriages. Watching my living child grow up. Naming the dead one Lily and planting her ashes under a lily flower in our front yard. Loving my family and extended family. Going to work as a prickly guy who now gets pulled into goo sometimes while watching fabric softener ads on TV. At that point, I knew my life had an inflection point in moving toward just right. Sometimes, it's just hard to accept how much it hurt getting there.

Just right is tricky, but we evolve. We swing back and forth. We try to grab it and it's gone. And we search because that's what being alive means. It's what the mystics say when we wake up and see all those wiggly lines.

I now go to work knowing that I can let Alec pull me into the goo a bit. It's okay to hang out and hold the space there. I'm fully awake in those moments and can appreciate my discomfort for what it is: self-awareness. There's no right or wrong, and that feels just right.

CHAPTER 13

CONCLUSION—CLOSING THOUGHTS AND THEMES ON JUST RIGHT

In his famous book *Man's Search for Meaning,* Viktor Frankl says, "An abnormal reaction to an abnormal situation is normal behavior." Following his logic, it's normal behavior to wonder how all the preceding chapters situate. Why would anybody put subjects such as nicotine, water, Newton's third law, drug pricing, and pop psychology into one book? How do these disconnected topics really relate to one another? And what are the grand themes or takeaways?

Let me try to address all three.

The subjects I chose were informed by my muse, the force of inspiration being a good guidepost for any big project. Finding superhero quotes, watching children's videos on YouTube, or looking at baseball cards was pretty easy—I promise, I'm an adult. Getting lost in baby Yoda videos on YouTube—again, still an adult—is fun, but, as you can imagine, not in service to a book project. Sometimes the muse needs guardrails, and book projects definitely help. Sometimes a way to do challenging things, especially on the subject of just right, is to just have a deadline.

As inspirations accumulated, some connections started to emerge. First, the Goldilocks Principle seemed bigger and broader than I think many realize. Remember, principles are fundamental truths, and I was noticing truths everywhere, from baby eye movements to the greenhouse gas effect. Then came the process of threading those connections into some type of coherent message. Some of those subjects made the book, while many others got left on the cutting room floor. Finally, there seemed to be something deeper gnawing at me—apparently, muses both inspire and bite—this idea of "just right" being a truth bigger than what science alone can explain. The caregiver stories and the chapters on death and religion sprung up from that deeper look. The result is the mash-up of topics included in the book.

At this point, it would be helpful to be more prescriptive about the themes covered. Call this the refrigerator, bulletin board, CliffNotes, or nightstand portion of the book. After coming this far, this is where one can choose their own adventure. Kind of fitting for a book about a fairy tale, right?

My hope is for everyone to refer back to this next section two months, two years, or twenty years from now. It's the evergreen chapter! Maybe it will spur rereading a passage where an idea needs further exploration. I don't expect all the themes to land with everyone in equal measure.

Twelve "just right" themes I encountered during my writing search follow. These may be helpful in your own search. I tried to get to ten, but I couldn't help myself.

Here they are in order of appearance:

1. **The Goldilocks Principle is in more places than expected (Background):**
   a. *Goldilocks and the Three Bears* introduces Goldilocks, who learns her "just right" lesson by being bold and

adventurous. It also provides a commentary on the "naughty girl" who'd be better off following the rules. The truth is a just right world needs plenty of both.

b. The power of threes in storytelling is a critical way of examining a "middle way" forward. Storytelling helps us understand science in ways that are relatable and applicable. The origin of the Goldilocks Principle is the intersection of science and storytelling to explain fundamental truths.

c. The examination of U-shaped curves in legume roots, when best to get married, how machines learn, ideal classroom sizes, and baby eye movements show how the Goldilocks Principle is within and all around us every day.

2. **Be curious in examining things for their smaller parts and larger meanings (Guts):**

a. We learned from Rich all the ways "guts" can manifest in a twenty-four-hour period. As he prepared to bury his wife during the beginning of the pandemic, he unconsciously encountered the digestion, essential, courage, and intuition meanings of the word were all important to help set a right path.

b. Examining words like guts can reveal misconceptions, like valuing one meaning of a word (courage) over another (intuition, essential). Just right is supported by legs on a stool, all needing to be of equal length. If we hold up one version of guts too high, the stool becomes lopsided, and we fall to the floor.

3. **Use numbers as a means of understanding both truth telling and storytelling (Numbers):**

a. We learned from Rich on the blood thinner medication all the ways numbers can leave us cold on the benefit of a treatment—number needed to treat—then leave us open when those numbers are reframed—relative benefit over a prolonged life. The truth was neither the medicine nor the evidence changed. The story was how Rich identified with the numbers in the context of his life.

  b. The truth is that different numbers representing the same reality can lead to vastly different outcomes. Saying something has a 95 percent chance of success or a 5 percent chance of failure often leads to much different decision-making. Holding these up in equal scale is critical.

4. <u>Dark alleys can reveal just right searches with treatments providing a way for the body to heal (Mental Health):</u>

  a. From Claire and Anne, we saw how depression, loneliness, and anxiety lead to dark states with—sometimes—harmful coping strategies, like smoking. The search can be challenging because the answers are not found along straight lines.

  b. Any mental health search can be aided by recognizing the power and limitations of medicines, the act of cradling to form its own U-shaped curve, and recognizing the body's ability to heal itself in the right circumstances.

5. <u>Embrace a desire to search for just right and accept when the search reflexively finds us (Withdrawal):</u>

  a. From Rob and Brian, we learned the power chemicals have to throw off the body's equilibrium and the body's natural tendency to find a new version of just right under the right conditions. For Rob, it was a lifetime of drinking followed by sobriety producing an informed perspective on the powerful effects of chemicals. For Brian, it was a lifetime of suffering and withdrawals followed by a new chemical offering a new way forward.

b. Newton's third law shows life's equal and opposite reactions can bring us closer to just right. Appreciating the "reflex" that is baked into the biology and physics all around us is critical to realizing how just right sometimes finds us.

6. **There is tension between action and fate (Head and Heart):**

a. We learned from Gus and Marilyn's sleep and heart troubles that some of our problems can be appreciated both intentionally and randomly. For Gus, it was being on five different sleep medicines and intentionally reducing his burden with precision. For Marilyn, it was appreciating how she somehow thrived into her eighties despite a medical history two miles long.

b. Leaning into our intentions and surrendering to fate's plan in equal measure is how we ground ourselves in any search for just right. Both can be uncomfortable but necessary.

7. **Understand that motivation, mystery, and margin are at the heart of any just right around money (Economics)**

a. Economic meaning can be found in understanding the motivational underpinning of "ice cream!" moments. It can also help us understand why Reeta and Sylvia can't afford to get their inhaler or insulin. Each of them struggles under the weight of a system too complex for them or anybody to understand.

b. A just right search means moving in the direction of simplicity, a counterforce to the additional complex layers where margin seems to be a prevailing motivation.

8. **Rely on people around (wisdom of crowds) and within (expertise) in a search for just right (Communication):**
   a. We learned from Sheila and Amina the power a crowd has when it becomes fragmented—as it did for Sheila recovering from surgery—and when it comes together—as it did for Amina, who needed help with her diabetes.
   b. Searching for the wisdom of crowds around us is in everything from jellybean guessing contests to the development of video games. The search for the wisdom within comes through time and perspective, as I explored in a personal story of grief. Its expertise simply by exploring the notion of "know thyself."

9. **Aiding a just right search may not require words. It may just be holding mirrors (Self-help):**
   a. We visited with Stan, who was in a state of disbelief about the power of a raspberry on his diabetes. It wasn't until a mirror was held up that he started to see a new version of himself. We explored the nature of competence and confidence in the Dunning-Kruger Effect, as well as the power of just right stress levels in performance.
   b. We reviewed how even exercise, seen by most only as right, has a just right, with daily strenuous exercise being somewhat harmful to heart health. Stress must be balanced with rest.

10. **Facts, feelings, and control are critical in understanding the relationship with our surroundings (Environment):**
    a. Roger's difficulty breathing revealed inconvenient truths about a home potentially impacting his health.

His search required examining the details—mold values, ventilation systems—as well as understanding the big pictures—moving, testing, installing home changes.

b. Our friend Victor Frankenstein did not have that zooming out perspective, much to his peril. Americans are at a similar Frankenstein crossroads in relationship to our surroundings. Don't be like Victor and be led by blind ambition with his head only the microscope. The search needs to include finding a mentor with some binoculars.

11. **Holding space for conviction and doubt is critical in any just right search (Religion):**

a. We explored the tension between certainty and doubt in Maria, who was running into doorways at 3 a.m. on sleep medications. She saw in me a religious conversion opportunity. I saw in her a means of better examining my own doubts. My certainty about her health moved her toward considering her family's concern. Her certainty of my reckoning moved me away from seeing conviction or doubt as static.

b. Appreciating middle and extreme viewpoints offers opportunities for strength, suffering, and clarity. Engaging in the ongoing tug-of-war means our role is to simply grab the rope.

12. **Embrace both the prickly (mechanistic) and the goo (mystical) views of the world (Death):**

a. We met Alec, the hippie, pot-smoking cancer patient, his existential "goo" running up against my "prickly" focused on his medication refills and blood pressure.

b. We experience our natural tendency toward prickly and goo during transformational moments, where a tug-of-war within results a new just right emerging from the ashes.

Maybe twelve themes are too many? Never fear because I've whittled the refrigerator, CliffNotes sized themes above down to an index card sized version with three—yes, three!— themes that follow. They are:

1. Just right words such as balance, equanimity, harmony, and equilibrium are within and all around us. Seeing the Goldilocks Principle in science and storytelling helps us appreciate it everywhere.

2. Just right aligns itself on spectrums and shapes—U-shaped curves and wiggly lines!—in the physical world as much as it does in our heads. This may seem both simple and difficult to cultivate in day-to-day life. I know I struggle in mine. Hopefully, my personal and caregiver stories served as reminders that spectrums, wiggly lines, and shapes take place all around us.

3. Just right involves a push and pull between states of being. They include intention and randomness (biology), conviction and doubt (religion), truth and story (numbers), big and small (guts), facts and feeling (environment), words and mirrors (self-help), search and found (withdrawal), and past and present (mental health). Finding where we are along these helps us better understand our relationship to what's around us.

A note about my own stories. I found it scary and liberating to write a version of my story down. I did not start this project intending to share anything personal, let alone share things *this* personal. Uff da. I've never been described as an open book—pardon the pun. It sort of just happened, a nod to the muse and moments—like the one I had with my wife Kerry when she asked me what's true—that offer inflection points toward change.

A few final notes before I go.

Having read this book, a fair question to ask would be: how would I define just right in one sentence? The simplest answer I can come up with is: "once we learn, we know." The "learn" was the reason for writing this book, the "know" being the feeling we get from knowledge in those specific moments. It's the accumulated wisdom of what's within and all around us.

At its core, this was intended to be an optimistic view of the world. In a world where divisiveness and grievances get the headlines, I'm buoyed by the idea that there are ties that bind within and all around us. I have no specific expertise other than the caregiver stories I tell, my own curiosity, and excitement at bringing "aha!" discoveries to the reader.

I found myself sanguine even when researching challenging topics like drug prices or the environment. Part of that was knowing there was a collective way forward worth searching for. Part of it was also knowing that just rights find us collectively, whether we're searching for them or not.

You might wonder why I had Taoist proverbs at the beginning of each of my chapters. I didn't explain the Tao or "the way," nor did I delve into it during my chapters on religion or death. I found the "Tao Te Ching" to be the thematic North Star during the writing of the book. For those who don't find the words useful, hopefully, it wasn't too distracting. As I covered in Chapter 11, there are many just right spiritual texts to draw upon for inspiration. The path from a raised Catholic to ancient Chinese philosophy shows our lines are indeed wiggly.

With all this, I hope you've enjoyed the journey. From the introduction, when Jim made the innocuous statement about wanting to feel "normal," I wanted to really understand how we individually and collectively notice it. Take this information forward to inspire conversations within yourself and others. If even one paragraph or chapter resonated, maybe your search for just right got a little easier. Best wishes on your own search. The good news is you don't have to look too far to begin.

ACKNOWLEDGMENTS

—

Writing a book took me to places I've never been, while mostly staring at a screen I hoped would fill up with words. The trip couldn't have been made without the time, talents, and treasures of some important people. The following will be an attempt to give their influence justice.

To my wife, Kerry Kresl, little did I know when we met all those years ago that I'd find my intellectual muse. I just thought you were cool and hot! Your encouragements, counsel, and "I never see you move" comments as I worked through these chapters will be what I remember most. You've always told me how it is (bad haircuts and all) and provided great feedback on the contents of this book. Most of all, your nudges to find my creative inspiration and to stay true to my inner voice leave me grateful beyond words. I never knew what a true partner was until I met you. Thank you for sticking with me every step of the way.

To my son, Jude Kresl, my prediction is that you'll cringe at these stories over the next five years and come to love them over the next fifty. Hopefully, your brief appearances serve as a time capsule of some of the best moments of my life. Thank you for your loving heart, big personality, and kind spirit. I couldn't have asked for a better title than being your father.

To my parents, Kevin and Mary Kresl, your support of my endeavors has never wavered. You asked questions about my book to both understand and be my biggest cheerleaders after our talks. Your feedback during the editing process helped change the book's tone and language. You're both everything a child could want, even as an adult. Thank you for being the "just right" parents for me.

To my extended family, in particular my sister, Katie Samuelson, brother-in-law, Chad Samuelson, and mother-in-law, Barb Schwenn. I'm forever thankful to exist in a family where we can share our lives together in fun, love, and relative harmony. Thank you for taking an interest in my book, in particular, my mother-in-law, who told me what she liked (the patient stories) and what she didn't like (my grammar and punctuation). Thank you for enriching my life.

To the patients whose stories I shared, your impact on the soul of this book is impossible to overstate. While your names and details were changed to protect your privacy, your quotes and candor were the heartbeat of this book. For years, I would scribble in my journal passages of our time as a way of sorting out your problems and my feelings. Little did I know, they were the seeds of a larger tree not yet come to life. Thank you for giving this project a chance to grow.

A quick note to one of my beta readers and coworkers, Jill Konstantinides. When I asked you to read some of the contents of my book for feedback, you were about to give birth to your first child, Claire. So much for "just right" timing. Your feedback during your maternity leave was critical during a time when I needed a clinician's perspective. Thank you for sharing your thoughts during such an important transition time for you and your family. It speaks to your generous spirit.

Special thanks to Jeff Shannon who reminded me how you never know when conversations lead to big changes. Jeff was generous enough to connect me to the Creative Institute, which started me in the book-writing process. He also shared his experiences writing his first book (*Hard Work Is Not Enough*, shout out) and gave me the firsthand accounts we all need when venturing into new territories. Thank you for being the just right catalyst at just the right time.

Like any great fisherman, Eric Koester and the Creator Institute deserve a big thanks. Eric's energy and direction during the early stages gave me hope that an aspiring writer could finish a book! Thank you for building the boat, paddle, and rod, and teaching this young fisherman how to fish on my own. I couldn't get through this book without making one Minnesota fisherman reference!

A big thank you to the publishing team at New Degree Press. Your know-how, enthusiasm, and professionalism gave me confidence in the thousands of moments a first-time author thinks, "I don't know how to do that." I'd like to give special thanks to my developmental editor, Trisha Giramma, and revisions editor, Sandy Huffman.

Trisha came first when the book was an incoherent mess of ideas and anecdotes. Her feedback was firm, fair, and encouraging. She found a "just right" of toughness and kindness that had me wondering if she was also a life coach. I'll be forever grateful to her for helping me get my first book green lit!

Sandy came in just as I was starting to fundraise for this book. Her encouragement, feedback, and "fixer" mindset gave me a full appreciation for all the things a good editor does. She told me from the beginning that she'd help me get to the finish line, and boy, she was not lying! Thank you for your laughter and keeping me on task along the way!

To all my campaign contributors: You preordered my book even before it was done. Some of you asked what it was about, while others, I'm sure, ordered it after endless harassment from me. Crowdfunding took me outside my comfort zone in ways I could barely imagine. It also lifted my spirits to know people felt I had a story to tell. Thank you kindly for the words and support.

Matthew Nugent,
Ghada Elnashar,
Lan Luu,
Sarah Simon,
Lana Barkawi,
Scott Pearson,
Claire McNeil,
Colleen Kingsbury,
Paul Kieser,
Mary Kresl,
Matt and Michelle Bergren,
Kelly Ruziska,
Michael Shonts,
Amie Jo Digatono,
Mike Waldt,
Emma Paskewitz,
Kent V. Bridgeman,
Jeremy Haase,
Claire Tralle,
Jacques Capesius,
Erin Wilcox,
Sarah Maryon Hayes,
Elaine Pearson,
Jared Parviz,

Patrick Sexton,
Victoria R. Schanen,
Brandon Yerxa,
Elizabeth von der Marwitz,
Rebekah Roemer,
Gwen Paulison,
Sandy Johnson,
Darlene Nyberg,
Tiffany Yerxa,
Maria Zarambo,
Tim Foley,
Karla Lindahl,
Krista Gens,
Caren Jacobs,
Jay Dahlstrom,
Laura Richardson,
Jean Anderson,
Steven Kastendieck,
John Doric,
Debra Dullinger,
Adam Kresl,
Hans Hennen,
Kassie Curtis-Yaeck,
Bryan Munsell,

Paul Glynn,
Emily Jones,
Elizabeth Beckman,
JoAnne Myhre,
Lisa Krohn,
Tim Gallagher,
Amanda Bisel,
David Kreft,
Emily Hein,
Anjanette Finnegan,
Jenna Knutson,
Jen Brandenburg,
Patricia Giramma,
Deeter Neumann,
Jessica Swearingen,
Constance Valdes-Tergas,
Eric Koester,
Danielle Wortman,
Elizabeth Kennedy,
Ken Paulison,
Mary Manns,
Ben Bache-Wiig,
Mike Arora,
Scott Roby,
Brittany Picard,
Kathryn Derner,
Alison Watkins Welshinger,
Michael Muskin,
Mark Sanford,
Kristi Fecik,
Melissa Carlsrud,
Andrew Tarleton,

Adriana Youssef,
Mckaya Kastner,
David Fuhs,
Rodney Umlas,
Tracy Anderson-Haag,
Jill Konstantinides,
Daniel Tipton,
Monique U. Betz,
Angel Becker,
Matthew Mullenbach,
Matthew Wolf,
Nathan Blake,
Barb Hintzen,
Deb Klein,
Andy Kock,
Ann Byre,
Kristi Gullickson,
Logan Hendrickson,
Paul Krogh,
Becky Fahrenbruch,
Barbara Schwenn,
Jill Strykowski,
Judy Ritter,
Mark G. Kresl,
Kiersten Anderson,
Stacey Ness,
Laura Simon Franzen,
Rebecca Warrior,
Amy L. Olson,
Dan Liebl,
Brent Schloe,
Dennis Timmermann,

Travis Sagedahl,
Adam Sagedahl,
Andy Schneider,
Stephen Mandt,
Matthew Brandel,
Rachel Root,
Tiffany Reinitz,
Jennifer Tam,
Jeff Shannon,
Lee T. Peterson,
Giselle Restrepo,

Adam Bakken,
Lindsay Hur,
Mary Nelson,
Kelly Gannon,
Kristen Elliott,
Nilanjana Banerji,
Bill and Ericka Pirkl,
Mike Brody,
Robin Hugo,
Sammy Samuelson,
Mary Herman

APPENDIX

INTRODUCTION

Davidson, Judy E., Ramona O. Hopkins, Deborah Louis, and Theodore J. Iwashyna. "Post-Intensive Care Syndrome." 2013. https://www.sccm.org/MyICUCare/THRIVE/Post-intensive-Care-Syndrome.

Diamandis, Peter H. "A Look at How Much Humanity Has Advanced over the Last 100 Years." Futurism. February 27, 2017. https://futurism.com/a-look-at-how-much-humanity-has-advanced-over-the-last-100-years.

Gilster, Paul. "On 300 Million Habitable Zone Planets." *Centauri Dreams*. November 10, 2020. https://www.centauri-dreams.org/2020/11/10/on-300-million-habitable-zone-planets/.

Herman, Rhett. "How Fast Is the Earth Moving?" *Scientific American*, October 26, 1998. https://www.scientificamerican.com/article/how-fast-is-the-earth-mov/.

Rosenthal, Elisabeth. "The Soaring Cost of a Simple Breath." *The New York Times*, October 12, 2013. https://www.nytimes.com/2013/10/13/us/the-soaring-cost-of-a-simple-breath.html.

Twenge, Jean M. "The Sad State of Happiness in the United States and the Role of Digital Media." *World Happiness Report, Chap-*

ter 5. March 20, 2019. https://worldhappiness.report/ed/2019/
the-sad-state-of-happiness-in-the-united-states-and-the-role-
of-digital-media/.

CHAPTER 1

Aarhus University. "Goldilocks Principle in Biology: Fine-Tuning
the 'Just Right' Signal Load." ScienceDaily. October 12, 2018.
http://www.sciencedaily.com/releases/2018/10/181012110155.htm.

Booker, Christopher. *The Seven Basic Plots: Why We Tell Stories.*
New York, NY: Continuum Books, 2004.

Borne, Kirk. "Are Your Predictive Models Like Broken Clocks?"
Rocket-Powered Data Science. January 25, 2016. http://rocket-
datascience.org/?p=497.

Fuchs, Jay (blog). "The Goldilocks Effect: What It Is & How to
Apply It." *Hubspot*, April 19, 2021. https://blog.hubspot.com/
sales/goldilocks-effect-pricing.

Gladwell, Malcolm. *David and Goliath: Underdogs, Misfits & the
Art of Battling Giants.* New York: Back Bay Books, 2015.

Hasa. "What Is the Moral of Goldilocks and the Three Bears."
Pediaa.com. May 20, 2016. https://pediaa.com/what-is-the-
moral-of-goldilocks-and-the-three-bears/.

Kidd, Celeste, Steven T. Piantadosi, and Richard N. Aslin. "The
Goldilocks Effect: Human Infants Allocate Attention to Visual
Sequences That Are Neither Too Simple nor Too Complex."
PloS ONE 7, no. 5 (May 23, 2012). https://doi.org/10.1371/journal.
pone.0036399.

Tearle, Dr. Oliver. "A Summary and Analysis of 'Goldilocks and
the Three Bears.'" *Interesting Literature,* 2022. https://interest-
ingliterature.com/2017/05/a-summary-and-analysis-of-goldi-
locks-and-the-three-bears/.

The English Schoolhouse Publishing. "The Ghanaian Goldilocks." October 16, 2014. Video, 17:42. https://www.youtube.com/watch?v=MWhSlX66fSw&t=32s.

Tolovaj Publishing House. "The History Behind the Story of Goldilocks." *Owlcation.* May 31, 2021. https://owlcation.com/humanities/goldilocks-and-three-bears.

Weissmann, Jordan. "The Goldilocks Theory of Marriage." *Slate,* July 16, 2015. https://slate.com/business/2015/07/getting-married-late-increases-your-chance-of-a-divorce.html.

Wolfinger, Nicholas H. "Want to Avoid Divorce? Wait to Get Married, But Not Too Long." *Institute for Family Studies,* July 16, 2015. https://ifstudies.org/blog/want-to-avoid-divorce-wait-to-get-married-but-not-too-long/.

CHAPTER 2

Beaugerie, Laurent, and Jean-Claude Petit. "Antibiotic-Associated Diarrhoea." *Best Practice & Research Clinical Gastroenterology* 18, no. 2 (April 2004): 337–52. https://doi.org/10.1016/j.bpg.2003.10.002.

Blake, Joan Salge. "Can We Really Eat Like Our Paleo Ancestors?" *Boston Globe,* November 2014. http://archive.boston.com/lifestyle/health/blog/nutrition/2014/11/can_we_really_eat_like_our_pal.html.

Cleveland Clinic. "Body Systems & Organs: Digestive System." Reviewed August 9, 2021. https://my.clevelandclinic.org/health/body/7041-digestive-system.

Denhard, Morgan. "Digestive Enzymes and Digestive Enzyme Supplements." *Johns Hopkins Medicine,* Accessed June 30, 2022. https://www.hopkinsmedicine.org/health/wellness-and-prevention/digestive-enzymes-and-digestive-enzyme-supplements.

Moshfegh, Alanna, Joseph Goldman, and Linda Cleveland. *What We Eat in America, NHANES 2001–2002: Usual Nutrient Intakes from Food Compared to Dietary Reference Intakes*. Washington, DC: US Dept of Agriculture, Agricultural Research Service, September 2005. https://www.ars.usda.gov/ARSUserFiles/80400530/pdf/0102/usualintaketables2001-02.pdf.

Villines, Zawn. "How Long Are the Intestines?" *Medical News Today*. February 8, 2021. https://www.medicalnewstoday.com/articles/how-long-are-your-intestines.

Zemeckis, Robert, dir. *Back to the Future*. 1985; Universal City, CA: Amblin Entertainment. https://www.imdb.com/title/tt0088763/characters/nm0000502.

CHAPTER 3

Australian Bureau of Statistics. "1014.0—Trust in ABS and ABS Statistics—A Survey of Informed Users and the General Community, 2020: Summary." The Community Trust in ABS Statistics Survey press release, July 20, 2020. https://www.abs.gov.au/ausstats/abs@.nsf/mf/1014.0.

Bektas, Metin. "NASA's O-Ring Problem and the Challenger Disaster." *Metin's Media and Math*. December 3, 2013. https://metinmediamath.wordpress.com/2013/12/03/nasas-o-ring-problem-and-the-challenger-disaster/.

Duronio, Ben, and Walt Hickey. "The 10 Most Important Numbers in the World." *Business Insider*, July 8, 2012. https://www.businessinsider.com/most-important-numbers-2012-7.

Encyclopaedia Britannica Online. s.v. "Challenger Disaster." Accessed June 29, 2022. https://www.britannica.com/event/Challenger-disaster.

Geckoboard (blog). "Five Sources of Misleading Statistics (and How They Can Jeopardize Your Company)." September 16, 2020.

https://www.geckoboard.com/blog/sources-of-misleading-statistics/.

Greger, Michael. "The True Benefits vs. Side Effects of Statins." NutritionFacts.org, August 25, 2021. Video, 5:30. https://nutritionfacts.org/video/the-true-benefits-vs-side-effects-of-statins/.

Lewis, Michael. *Moneyball: The Art of Winning an Unfair Game.* New York: W.W. Norton & Company, 2003.

Mendes, Diego, Carlos Alves, and Francisco Batel-Marques. "Number Needed to Treat (NNT) in Clinical Literature: An Appraisal." *BMC Medicine* 15, no. 112 (June 1, 2017). https://doi.org/10.1186/s12916-017-0875-8.

Mitchell, Amy, Jeffrey Gottfried, Galen Stocking, Mason Walker, and Sophia Fedeli. "Many Americans Say Made-Up News Is a Critical Problem That Needs to Be Fixed." *Pew Research Center*, June 5, 2019. https://www.pewresearch.org/journalism/2019/06/05/many-americans-say-made-up-news-is-a-critical-problem-that-needs-to-be-fixed/.

Orem, Tina. "Survey Reveals Significant Distrust Around Data Collection." *Credit Union Times*, November 19, 2019. https://www.cutimes.com/2019/11/19/survey-reveals-significant-distrust-around-data-collection/.

Pressfield, Steven. *The War of Art: Break Through the Blocks and Win Your Inner Creative Battles.* New York: Black Irish Entertainment LLC, 2012.

Teitel, Amy Shira. "What Caused the Challenger Disaster?" History.com. Updated January 28, 2022. https://www.history.com/news/how-the-challenger-disaster-changed-nasa.

Twain, Mark. "Mark Twain: Quotes—Quotable Quote." Goodreads.com. Accessed June 29, 2022. https://www.goodreads.com/

quotes/100106-facts-are-stubborn-things-but-statistics-are-pliable.

US Congress. House. Committee on Science and Technology. *Investigation of the Challenger Accident.* 99th Cong., 2nd sess., October 29, 1986. https://www.govinfo.gov/content/pkg/GPO-CRPT-99hrpt1016/pdf/GPO-CRPT-99hrpt1016.pdf.

Woodfill, Jerry. "How and Why Did the Challenger Explode?" Space Educators' Handbook (OMB/NASA Report Number S677). Houston, TX: NASA Johnson Space Center, 1989. Accessed June 29, 2022. https://er.jsc.nasa.gov/seh/explode.html.

CHAPTER 4

InformedHealth.org. "Depression: How Effective Are Antidepressants?" Cologne, Germany: Institute for Quality and Efficiency in Health Care, Updated June 18, 2020. https://www.ncbi.nlm.nih.gov/books/NBK361016/.

Julien, Robert M., Claire Advokat, and Joseph E. Comaty. *Julien's Primer of Drug Action.* 13th ed. New York: Worth Publishers, 2020.

Morin, Amy. "Loneliness Is as Lethal as Smoking 15 Cigarettes Per Day. Here's What You Can Do About It." *Inc Magazine,* June 18, 2018. https://www.inc.com/amy-morin/americas-loneliness-epidemic-is-more-lethal-than-smoking-heres-what-you-can-do-to-combat-isolation.html.

CHAPTER 5

Julien, Robert M., Claire Advokat, and Joseph E. Comaty. *Julien's Primer of Drug Action.* 13th ed. New York: Worth Publishers, 2020.

Lawal, Oluwadolapo D., Justin Gold, Amala Murthy, Rupam Ruchi, Egle Bavry, Anne L. Hume, Adam K. Lewkowitz,

Todd Brothers, and Xuerong Wen. "Rate and Risk Factors Associated with Prolonged Opioid Use after Surgery: A Systematic Review and Meta-Analysis." *JAMA Network Open* 3, no. 6 (2020): e207367. https://doi.org/10.1001/jamanetworkopen.2020.7367.

Lembke, Anna. *Dopamine Nation: Finding Balance in the Age of Indulgence.* New York: E.P. Dutton, 2021.

Mulder, P. "Pain Pleasure Curve." Toolshero.com, Updated March 25, 2022. https://www.toolshero.com/marketing/pain-pleasure-curve/.

The Physics Classroom. "Newton's Laws—Lesson 4—Newton's Third Law of Motion." Accessed June 29, 2022. https://www.physicsclassroom.com/class/newtlaws/Lesson-4/Newton-s-Third-Law.

CHAPTER 6

Cleveland Clinic. "How Does Blood Flow through Your Body?" Cleveland Clinic Health Library: Articles, Reviewed April 30, 2019. https://my.clevelandclinic.org/health/articles/17059-how-does-blood-flow-through-your-body.

Cleveland Clinic. "Insomnia." Cleveland Clinic Health Library: Diseases and Conditions, Reviewed October 15, 2020. Accessed June 29, 2022. https://my.clevelandclinic.org/health/diseases/12119-insomnia.

Kulkarni, Anandita, Anurag Mehta, Eugene Yang, and Biljana Parapid. "Older Adults and Hypertension: Beyond the 2017 Guideline for Prevention, Detection, Evaluation, and Management of High Blood Pressure in Adults." American College of Cardiology expert analysis, February 26, 2020. https://www.acc.org/latest-in-cardiology/articles/2020/02/26/06/24/older-adults-and-hypertension.

Osborne, Hannah. "Do Cats Have Nine Lives? The Myth Explained." *Newsweek*, October 29, 2021. https://www.newsweek.com/cats-nine-lives-myth-explained-1643381.

Resolve to Save Lives. "Controlling High Blood Pressure Will Save Millions of Lives." Accessed June 29, 2022. https://resolvetosavelives.org/cardiovascular-health/hypertension.

StarWars.com *editorial staff.* "The StarWars.com 10: Best Yoda Quotes." November 26, 2013. https://www.starwars.com/news/the-starwars-com-10-best-yoda-quotes.

US Department of Transportation. "Highway History: Interstate Frequently Asked Questions." Federal Highway Administration, Updated April 27, 2021. https://www.fhwa.dot.gov/interstate/faq.cfm.

Walker, Matthew. *Why We Sleep: Unlocking the Power of Sleep and Dreams.* New York: Scribner, 2017.

Wolk, Robert, Abu S. M. Shamsuzzaman, and Virend K. Somers. "Obesity, Sleep Apnea, and Hypertension." *Hypertension* 42 (November 10, 2003): 1067–74. https://doi.org/10.1161/01.HYP.0000101686.98973.A3.

Zapata, Kimberly. "100+ Insomnia Quotes for When Those Long, Restless Nights Feel Like They'll Never End." *Parade*, June 11, 2022. https://parade.com/1104448/kimberlyzapata/insomnia-quotes/.

CHAPTER 7

Centers for Disease Control and Prevention. "Insurance Coverage and Barriers to Care for People with Asthma." CDC.gov, Reviewed May 3, 2013. https://www.cdc.gov/asthma/asthma_stats/insurance_coverage.htm

Cussen, Mark P. "Top Five Reasons Why People Go Bankrupt." *Investopedia*, Updated March 4, 2021. https://www.investopedia.com/financial-edge/0310/top-5-reasons-people-go-bankrupt.aspx.

Diabetes UK. "100 Years of Insulin." Accessed June 29, 2022. https://www.diabetes.org.uk/research/research-impact/insulin.

Diener, Ed, and Robert Biswas-Diener. *Happiness: Unlocking the Mysteries of Psychological Wealth.* Hoboken, NJ: Wiley-Blackwell Publishing, 2008.

Entis, Laura. "Why Does Medicine Cost So Much? Here's How Drug Prices Are Set." *Time*, April 9, 2019. https://time.com/5564547/drug-prices-medicine/.

IQVIA Inc. "Understanding Insulin Market Dynamics in Low- and Middle-Income Countries." *The IQVIA Institute for Human Data Science Reports*, August 26, 2021. https://www.iqvia.com/insights/the-iqvia-institute/reports/understanding-insulin-market-dynamics-in-low-and-middle-income-countries.

Johnson, Eric, Ron Hassin, Tom Baker, Allison Bajger, and Galen Treuer. "Can Consumers Make Affordable Care Affordable? The Value of Choice Architecture." *University of Pennsylvania, Institute for Law & Economics* research paper, no. 13-28, *Columbia Business School* research paper, no. 13-56 (Revised January 24, 2014). http://dx.doi.org/10.2139/ssrn.2291598.

Johnson, Eric J., and Shankar Vedantam. "Choose Carefully." Accessed June 29, 2022. In *Hidden Brain*. Produced by Tara Boyle. Podcast, MP3 audio, 49:46. https://hiddenbrain.org/podcast/choose-carefully/.

Marsh, Tori. "Here's Why Asthma Inhalers Are So Expensive." *GoodRx Inc.*, Updated June 8, 2020. https://www.goodrx.com/conditions/asthma/heres-why-asthma-inhalers-are-so-expensive.

Mikulic, Matej. "Price Disparities for Top Product Advair Diskus US vs International 2022." Statista.com, March 28, 2022. https://www.statista.com/statistics/318363/prices-for-advair-diskus-in-the-us-and-abroad/.

Mitchell, Olivia S. "A Financial Literacy Test That Works." *Forbes,* December 14, 2017. https://www.forbes.com/sites/pensionresearchcouncil/2017/12/14/a-financial-literacy-test-that-works/?sh=25913f10641f.

Robin, Vicki, and Joe Dominguez. *Your Money or Your Life: Nine Steps to Transforming Your Relationship with Money and Achieving Financial Independence.* London: Penguin Books, 2008.

Rosenthal, Elisabeth. "The Soaring Cost of a Simple Breath." *The New York Times,* October 12, 2013. https://www.nytimes.com/2013/10/13/us/the-soaring-cost-of-a-simple-breath.html.

Stanley, Tiffany. "Life, Death, and Insulin." *Washington Post Magazine,* January 7, 2019. https://www.washingtonpost.com/news/magazine/wp/2019/01/07/feature/insulin-is-a-lifesaving-drug-but-it-has-become-intolerably-expensive-and-the-consequences-can-be-tragic/.

Thomas, Katie. "The Complex Math behind Spiraling Prescription Drug Prices." *The New York Times,* April 27, 2016. https://www.nytimes.com/2016/04/28/business/high-drug-prices-explained.html.

CHAPTER 8

Clear, James (blog). "How Experts Practice Better Than the Rest." Accessed June 30, 2022. https://jamesclear.com/deliberate-practice-strategy.

Frandsen, Brigham R., Karen E. Joynt, James B. Rebitzer, and Ashish K. Jha. "Care Fragmentation, Quality, and Costs Among Chronically Ill Patients." *The American Journal of Man-*

aged Care 21, no. 5 (May 2015). https://www.ajmc.com/view/care-fragmentation-quality-costs-among-chronically-ill-patients.

Powers, Brian W., Farhad Modarai, Sandeep Palakodeti, Manisha Sharma, Nupur Mehta, Sachin H. Jain, and Vivek Garg. "Impact of Complex Care Management on Spending and Utilization for High-Need, High-Cost Medicaid Patients." *The American Journal of Managed Care* 26, no. 2 (February 2020). https://www.ajmc.com/view/impact-of-complex-care-management-on-spending-and-utilization-for-highneed-highcost-medicaid-patients

Schmidt, Gregory MD (blog). "Healthcare Fragmentation: Focus on the Patients, and the Data Will Follow." June 6, 2019. http://www.gregoryschmidt.ca/writing/healthcare-fragmentation.

Surowiecki, James. *The Wisdom of Crowds: Why the Many Are Smarter Than the Few and How Collective Wisdom Shapes Business, Economies, Societies and Nations.* New York: Doubleday, 2004.

Webber, Emily (blog). "Social Group Sizes, Dunbar's Number and Implications for Communities of Practice." May 3, 2020. https://emilywebber.co.uk/social-group-sizes-dunbars-number-and-implications-for-communities-of-practice/.

Yang, Jenny. "Medicare—Statistics & Facts." Statista.com, February 16, 2022. https://www.statista.com/topics/1167/medicare/.

CHAPTER 9

Gino, Francesco. "Are You Too Stressed to Be Productive? Or Not Stressed Enough?" *Harvard Business Review*, April 14, 2016. https://hbr.org/2016/04/are-you-too-stressed-to-be-productive-or-not-stressed-enough.

Gough, Christina. "Gym, Health & Fitness Club Industry Revenue in the United States 2011–2021." Statista.com, January 28, 2021.

https://www.statista.com/statistics/605223/us-fitness-health-club-market-size-2007-2021/

LaRosa, John (blog). "$10.4 Billion Self-Improvement Market Pivots to Virtual Delivery During the Pandemic." Market-Research.com, August 2, 2021. https://blog.marketresearch.com/10.4-billion-self-improvement-market-pivots-to-virtual-delivery-during-the-pandemic.

Nietzsche, Friedrich. *The Portable Nietzsche.* Edited and translated by Walter Kaufmann. London: Penguin Books, 1988.

O'Keefe, James H., Evan L. O'Keefe, and Carl J. Lavie. "The Goldilocks Zone for Exercise: Not Too Little, Not Too Much." *Missouri Medicine* 115, no. 2 (2018): 98–105. https://www.ncbi.nlm.nih.gov/pmc/articles/PMC6139866/.

Psychology Today. "Dunning-Kruger Effect." Accessed June 30, 2022. https://www.psychologytoday.com/us/basics/dunning-kruger-effect.

Wirth, Michelle M. "Hormones, Stress, and Cognition: The Effects of Glucocorticoids and Oxytocin on Memory." *Adaptive Human Behavior and Physiology* 1 (2015): 177–201. https://doi.org/10.1007/s40750-014-0010-4.

CHAPTER 10

Bayram, A. Burcu, and Todd Shields. "Who Trusts the WHO? Heuristics and Americans' Trust in the World Health Organization During the COVID-19 Pandemic." *Social Science Quarterly* 102, no. 5 (April 29, 2021). https://doi.org/10.1111/ssqu.12977

Buis, Alan. "Steamy Relationships: How Atmospheric Water Vapor Supercharges Earth's Greenhouse Effect." NASA.gov, February 8, 2022. https://climate.nasa.gov/ask-nasa-climate/3143/steamy-relationships-how-atmospheric-water-vapor-supercharges-earths-greenhouse-effect/

Drah, Hermina. "21 Critical Mold Statistics We Have to Be Aware of in 2022." ComfyLiving.net, January 20, 2022. https://comfyliving.net/mold-statistics/

Haddeland, Ingjerd, Jens Heinke, Hester Biemans, Stephanie Eisner, Martina Flörke, Naota Hanasaki, Markus Konzmann, Fulco Ludwig, Yoshimitsu Masaki, Jacob Schewe, Tobias Stacke, Zachary D. Tessler, Yoshihide Wada, and Dominik Wisser. "Global Water Resources Affected by Human Interventions and Climate Change." *Proceedings of the National Academy of Sciences* 111, no. 9 (December 16, 2013): 3251–6. https://doi.org/10.1073/pnas.1222475110.

History.com Editors. "This Day in History: Mary Shelley's 'Frankenstein' is Published." *A&E Television Networks.* Updated December 30, 2019. https://www.history.com/this-day-in-history/frankenstein-published.

Kennedy, Brian, Alex Tyson, and Cary Funk. "Americans' Trust in Scientists, Other Groups Declines." *Pew Research Center,* February 15, 2022. https://www.pewresearch.org/science/2022/02/15/americans-trust-in-scientists-other-groups-declines/.

Merriam Webster. s.v. "Environment (n.)." Accessed June 30, 2022. https://www.merriam-webster.com/dictionary/environment.

NASA. "What Is the Greenhouse Effect?" Accessed June 30, 2022. https://climate.nasa.gov/faq/19/what-is-the-greenhouse-effect/

National Center for Healthy Housing. "Health Hazards, Prevention, and Solutions: Mold." Accessed June 30, 2022. https://nchh.org/information-and-evidence/learn-about-healthy-housing/health-hazards-prevention-and-solutions/mold/

National Park Service. "Yellowstone: Birth of a National Park." Updated February 5, 2020. https://www.nps.gov/yell/learn/historyculture/yellowstoneestablishment.htm.

Shelley, Mary. *Frankenstein: The 1818 Text*. London: Penguin Classics, 2018.

CHAPTER 11

Beres, Derek. "New Study Reveals Which People Fear Death the Least." *NeuroPsych*, March 26, 2017. https://bigthink.com/neuropsych/fear-of-death/.

Boorstein, Michelle. "American Secularism Is Growing—and Growing More Complicated." *The Washington Post*, January 14, 2022. https://www.washingtonpost.com/religion/2022/01/14/secularism-atheism-religion-nones/.

Raimi, Sam, dir. *Spider-Man 3*. 2007; Culver City, CA: Columbia Pictures.

Smith, Gregory A. "About Three-in-Ten US Adults Are Now Religiously Unaffiliated." *Pew Research Center*, December 14, 2021. https://www.pewresearch.org/religion/2021/12/14/about-three-in-ten-u-s-adults-are-now-religiously-unaffiliated/.

CHAPTER 12

Alan Watts Organization. "Life of Alan Watts." Accessed June 30, 2022. https://alanwatts.org/life-of-alan-watts/.

Mind Like the Sky blog. "'Gooey Prickles and Prickly Goo': Alan Watts on our Two Models of Reality and the Nature of Consciousness." December 1, 2013. https://mindlikethesky.com/2013/12/01/gooey-prickles-and-prickly-goo-alan-watts-on-our-two-models-of-reality-and-the-nature-of-consciousness/.

Sutter, Paul. "Is It a Wave or a Particle? It's Both, Sort Of." Space.com *Expert Voices: Op-Ed and Insights*, September 30, 2019.

CONCLUSION

Frankl, Viktor E. *Man's Search for Meaning.* Boston: Beacon Press, 2006.

Made in the USA
Monee, IL
01 December 2022

19115844R10134